THE ULTIMATE
SHADOW WORK
JOURNAL & WORKBOOK

2 Books in 1

A Comprehensive Collection of Exercises, Prompts, and Affirmations for Profound Self-Discovery, Emotional Recovery, and Personal Growth

LEIGH W. HART

401
Publishing

The Ultimate Shadow Work Journal & Workbook is a compilation of:

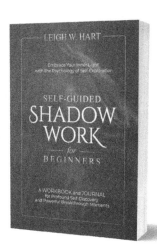

SELF-GUIDED SHADOW WORK FOR BEGINNERS

A WORKBOOK and JOURNAL for Profound Self-Discovery and Powerful Breakthrough Moments

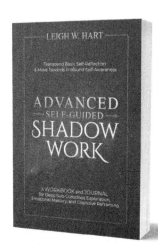

ADVANCED SELF-GUIDED SHADOW WORK

A WORKBOOK and JOURNAL for Deep Sub-Conscious Exploration, Emotional Mastery, and Cognitive Reframing

Table of Contents

Table of Contents

Elevate Your Journey With...

Bonus #1

THREE COMPLIMENTARY SUPPORT WORKBOOKS!

Self-Assessment Tests, Printable Affirmations & Bonus Materials:

As you begin your shadow work journey, are you unsure where to focus your efforts? Use the self-assessment tests to determine which areas of your life need the most attention. Plus, **60+** pages of additional worksheets and bonus materials.

Go to:
Shadow.LeighWHart.com
to receive your BONUS printable support materials.

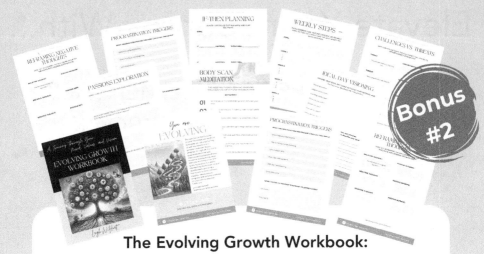

Bonus #2

The Evolving Growth Workbook:

Designed to revisit insights learned, reevaluate your progress, and continue evolving on your path to personal fulfillment.

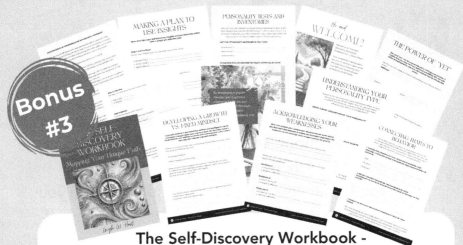

Bonus #3

The Self-Discovery Workbook - Mapping Your Unique Path:

Increased self-awareness leads to making choices that are true to who you are. It helps you live and lead with purpose and authenticity.

Go to:

Shadow.LeighWHart.com

to receive your BONUS printable support materials.

Trigger Warning:

This book explores the depths of the human psyche through the process of shadow work. While this transformative journey can be profoundly healing, it may also bring to the surface challenging and triggering thoughts or emotions. Topics covered in this book may include but are not limited to: trauma, inner conflicts, and unresolved emotions.

We encourage you to engage with this material at your own pace and discretion. If at any point you find yourself feeling overwhelmed or in need of support, please consider reaching out to a mental health professional or a trusted person in your life. Your well-being is of utmost importance.

Remember that you have the power to pause, reflect, and seek assistance whenever you feel it's necessary. You're not alone on this path, and there is help available.

Medical Disclaimer :

The content provided in this book is intended for educational and informational purposes. It is not a substitute for professional mental health advice, diagnosis, or treatment. Always consult with a qualified mental health professional or healthcare provider for personalized guidance regarding your specific mental health concerns. The author and publisher of this book do not endorse or recommend any specific therapies, medications, or interventions, and any decisions made based on the information presented in this book are at the reader's discretion and sole responsibility.

SELF-GUIDED SHADOW WORK FOR BEGINNERS

A WORKBOOK and JOURNAL
For Profound Self-Discovery
and Powerful Breakthrough Moments

LEIGH W. HART

Introduction

Have you ever had someone say to you, "I understand how you feel," and wonder how? There is no way for another person to understand your emotions, your pain, your frustration...your anything because it belongs only to you.

I will not utter those words, but I do empathize, and I want to help you better understand. As you stand on the edge of shadow work, it's natural to feel a sense of apprehension. The term itself can evoke feelings of ominousness and uncertainty, sending a shiver down your spine. It's okay to feel this way. I want you to know that it is normal.

Let's talk about Liz, who, in many ways, reflects the struggles that may have led you here today. Liz found herself trapped in an endless cycle of unhealthy relationships, constantly repeating patterns that left her feeling shattered and adrift. She made choices that led her down a destructive path, sometimes teetering on the edge of addiction. Her yearning for a way out was palpable.

Liz went to a few sessions of therapy, but finances limited her time there. She had grappled with these struggles for years, feeling isolated in her pain. The thought of exploring her shadows was exhausting, and she wondered if it might only bring more darkness into her life.

But then something shifted. Liz decided to take a chance on shadow work, just as you are considering now. As she started down this path, she began to notice small, positive shifts in her life. The overwhelming weight of her past started to lift slowly but surely. She realized that she could move forward at her own pace, creating support systems to navigate this journey of self-discovery on her own.

Now, let's talk about you. You may be facing things similar to Liz, struggling to control a torrent of unwanted emotions—anxiety, fear, guilt, sadness, exhaustion, and perhaps even depression. You've been searching for answers, yearning for personal growth and self-healing, but traditional paths may seem out of reach or overwhelming. The concept of shadow work can be intimidating and laden with questions and uncertainties.

Is shadow work safe? Is it ethical, helpful, and a positive experience? Can you do it on your own? How do you safeguard against re-traumatization? How do you cope with the fear and anxiety that often accompany this process? How can you track your progress, and what do you do if you feel stuck?

I want to assure you that all these questions will be addressed within the pages of this workbook. This is a secure and safe space for you to explore your shadow self and navigate the challenges that arise. Many others have walked this path before you, emerging on the other side with increased strength and self-awareness.

So, what led you to pick up this book? It is quite possible your longing for change, your desire to break free from binding patterns, and your yearning for a brighter, healthier future. If this is why you're here, I want you to know I support you.

By reading and using this workbook, you will acquire practical tools and insights that will help you to:

- ✓ Be guided on how to start shadow work, even as a beginner.
- ✓ Structure your self-analysis for maximum effectiveness.
- ✓ Identify and understand your shadow self.
- ✓ Cultivate self-acceptance and forgiveness.
- ✓ Harness the power of affirmations.
- ✓ Navigate self-guided therapy with confidence.
- ✓ Safely explore and heal past traumas.

In this moment, I want you to envision a life where you are in control of your emotions and where you no longer feel overwhelmed by anxiety, fear, or guilt. Picture yourself making choices that nurture your well-being, freeing yourself from the shackles of your past, and making your own path to a safe, peaceful future.

As the author, I come to you with a background in psychology and personal development, committed to providing you with credible, easy-to-follow guidance. I see you and the difficulties you face in finding your way to the life you deserve, and that's precisely what I aim to provide.

In this workbook, you'll find 80% practical tips and workbook activities that you can immediately put into practice, backed by 10% research and studies supporting the information and complemented by 10% relatable stories that resonate with your experiences.

Together, we will illuminate the shadows, carve the path ahead, and empower you to reclaim control over your life. This is the right book for you, and I'm eager to accompany you on this transformative adventure.

Let's get started.

CHAPTER 1
MASKS AND SHADOWS

Masks and Shadows

> *The shadow is needed now more than ever. We heal the world when we heal ourselves, and hope shines brightest when it illuminates the dark.* **–Sasha Graham**

We're about to start a trip into the world of shadow work together, exploring the depths of our inner selves step-by-step. This chapter is like the solid ground beneath your feet, providing the foundation you need to begin.

But what exactly is shadow work? Don't worry; I intend to keep this as simple as possible. Shadow work is a process rooted in the ideas of Carl Jung, a famous psychologist. It's all about shining a light on the parts of us we've kept hidden or ignored—those bits that might make us uncomfortable or that we've labeled as bad or unacceptable (Villines, 2022).

Here's the good news: Shadow work isn't about blaming ourselves, feeling broken, or thinking we're strange. It's not about making us feel ashamed or judged. Instead, it's a way to discover more about ourselves, be kind to ourselves, and become better versions of who we already are. It's about acknowledging that we all have shadows, and that's okay.

As we move through this chapter, I want to give you a background to what shadow work is, Jungian principles, the misconceptions behind the method, and why self-guided shadow work can be beneficial. I'll be your guide, and together, we'll look at practical tips and workbook activities that you can easily use in your life.

John's Encounter With His Shadow: A Personal Journey

It was a solemn day for John. He had just laid his father to rest, and the weight of grief hung heavily in the air. After the funeral, John's family and close relatives gathered at his childhood home for a small celebration of life, seeking solace in shared memories and a few drinks. It was meant to be a time of comfort and connection.

But life often has a way of surprising us, doesn't it?

As the evening wore on, a seemingly innocent comment from his cousin Chuck triggered an unexpected reaction from John. In an instant, he found himself grabbing Chuck's shirt and pulling him close, his voice laced with anger and frustration. It was a side of himself he had never witnessed before—a surge of power, raw and untamed. He felt like a character from a movie, the intimidating mob boss.

John's children offered reassurances, citing his grief as the reason for his outburst, but deep down, he couldn't excuse his own behavior. He knew that this wasn't who he wanted to be.

This, my friend, is what we call "The Shadow."

We all have a tendency to present a carefully curated version of ourselves to the world—an image that's pleasant, agreeable, and socially acceptable, much like tidying up our home before guests arrive. Yet, in the corners of our psyche are those unsavory traits we'd rather keep hidden—anger, jealousy, greed. These aspects of ourselves are like classified files, shuffled away into a folder labeled "My Shadow" and promptly forgotten, banished to the depths of our unconscious minds. And so, our comfort zone remains seemingly intact.

But for John, that moment of intense anger was a wake-up call. It forced him to confront a part of himself he had long suppressed—a part he had consigned to the shadows.

John's journey into shadow work had begun, and it would change his life forever.

Now, you might be wondering, "What exactly is this 'shadow work'?" As I mentioned, it's a concept deeply rooted in Jungian psychology, and it's all about embracing and integrating those hidden aspects of ourselves—the good, the bad, and the ugly. It's not about self-blame or labeling ourselves as broken; instead, it's a path to self-awareness and healing.

So, if you're feeling reluctant, afraid, or alone on this path of shadow work, remember that you're not the only one. Together, we'll navigate the uncharted territory of our inner selves, providing you with a safe and inviting space to explore your shadows, understand them, and ultimately, find a healthier balance within yourself. It's a journey worth taking, and we're here to guide you every step of the way.

The Shadow Self

It is important to distinguish your inner shadow traits, and I have included an exercise on how to embrace your shadow self.

Shadow work exercises are like treasure hunts for the parts of ourselves we've hidden away. The theory behind them is pretty simple: by bringing these hidden characteristics into the light of our consciousness, we can weaken their negative influence on our behavior and prevent them from sabotaging our lives.

Exercise: Noticing Emotional Reactions

Emotional reactions are like our inner alarm system. They're our immediate responses when we're not thinking logically. It's crucial to pay attention to them because they carry vital information about our shadow.

In this exercise, start by noticing when you experience intense emotions. Look for patterns and try to identify what triggers these emotional reactions. Here are some questions to help you along the way.

> **Write down any specific words, actions, situations, or people that trigger your emotional reactions.**

_____

_____

_____

_____

_____

> **Jot down how you reacted physically and, more importantly, what feelings were driving those physical reactions.**

_____

_____

_____

_____

_____

 > **As you think about why you felt that way, can you trace these feelings back to their origins? Write down what you uncover.**

_____

_____

_____

_____

_____

Once you've identified your triggers, or if you were already aware of them, you can move on to the next step. Now, this part can be a bit challenging. You need to be objective and dispassionate, which is easier said than done when you're feeling upset.

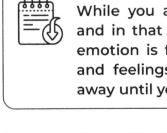 **While you are still feeling all those emotions and in that state of anger, fear, whatever that emotion is for you, write down your thoughts and feelings. Then, take a moment and step away until you've cooled down.**

_____

_____

_____

_____

_____

_____

_____

 When you're ready, revisit your triggers and emotional reactions. Consider where these reactions originated. Here's the tough part: validate your feelings by acknowledging that, in the context of their origins, they might be rational. Then, calmly, logically, and reasonably, write about whether they're still rational in the context of what triggered them.

By working through this exercise, you're beginning the journey of understanding and embracing your shadow self. Remember, it's all about self-discovery and self-compassion.

Where Does Shadow Work Come From?

I wanted to offer you five quick and intriguing facts about Jung and shadow work (Othon, 2017):

1 **Carl Jung's early passion:** Jung initially studied medicine but later followed his passion for understanding the human mind. He founded analytical psychology, which became the foundation for shadow work.

2 **The shadow metaphor:** Jung used the term "shadow" to describe the unconscious part of our minds, containing all the aspects of ourselves that we aren't aware of or choose to hide.

3 **Archetypes and symbols:** Jung believed that our unconscious minds contain universal symbols and archetypes that influence our thoughts, feelings, and behaviors. These archetypes are like primal blueprints for human experiences.

4 **Individuation process:** Jung believed that embracing our shadow selves is a crucial step in becoming our true selves. He called this process "individuation," where we integrate our hidden aspects to achieve wholeness.

5 **Influence on modern psychology:** Jung's ideas have had a profound impact on modern psychology, particularly in the realms of personality theory, dream analysis, and, of course, shadow work.

 Jungian Archetypes-What Are They?

Now, let's take a closer look at Jungian archetypes. These are like the characters in the story of our lives, influencing how we think, feel, and act. Here's a brief description of a few key archetypes:

1 **The Hero:** The hero within us is courageous, determined, and always seeking adventure. They're driven by a desire to conquer challenges and make the world a better place.

2 **The Shadow:** As we're focusing on shadow work, it's important to mention this one. The Shadow represents the hidden, dark side of ourselves. It contains the aspects we've repressed or denied. Embracing the shadow is a central aspect of shadow work.

3 **The Lover:** The lover archetype is passionate, sensual, and seeks deep connections with others. It's the part of us that craves intimacy and meaningful relationships.

4 **The Sage:** The sage is wise, knowledgeable, and constantly seeking truth and understanding. It's the part of us that loves learning and seeks wisdom.

5 **The Jester:** This archetype is all about joy, humor, and living in the moment. The jester reminds us not to take life too seriously and to find laughter even in the darkest times.

Why Do I Need My Shadow Side?

You might be wondering why we should even bother with this shadow stuff. Well, it's essential, and here's why.

Remember, your shadow self is like a hidden room within you. It's where you've stashed away parts of yourself that you're not quite comfortable with or have been conditioned to reject. Despite being tucked away, this is still a part of who you are. This room may be filled with aspects that:

◆ **Scare us:** These are the facets of ourselves that send shivers down our spine. It could be the anger, jealousy, or vulnerability we'd rather not acknowledge.

◆ **Are linked to past trauma:** Sometimes, the shadow is intricately connected to painful memories from the past. These recollections can be like locked doors waiting to be opened.

◆ **Cause embarrassment, guilt, or shame:** We all have traits or actions that make us cringe with embarrassment or feel guilty and ashamed. These are often tucked away in the shadows, out of sight.

◆ **We don't want to face:** Confronting our shadow self can be daunting. It's like that cluttered closet we avoid, hoping it will magically tidy itself up.

I need you to try and understand that your shadow isn't all doom and gloom. In fact, it can hold things you've neglected. Perhaps you've always had an artistic soul but chose a "safe" career in accounting. Your creativity might be hidden away in that shadow room.

Sometimes, even positive traits end up in the shadows if they are dismissed or belittled by others. For instance, if someone told you that your sensitivity was a flaw, you might have buried it deep within.

Now, let's explore why it's so vital we embrace your shadow self:

- **Achieve personal growth:** When we confront our fears and limitations, we create room for personal growth. It's like nurturing a plant in the sunlight; you'll see it flourish.

- **Heal from past trauma:** Addressing past wounds may be painful, but it's a vital step in your healing journey. It's like cleaning out the dust and cobwebs in that hidden room.

- **Release guilt and shame:** Letting go of negative emotions tied to your shadow is incredibly liberating. It's like finally tossing out the old, worn-out items from that cluttered closet.

- **Reconnect with your true self:** Those positive traits and passions lurking in your shadow are part of your authentic self. Embracing them can bring you happiness and fulfillment that you didn't even know was possible.

You are not broken, weird, or odd for having a shadow self. Remember, we all have one, and it's an essential part of our human experience. Owning your shadow is an act of courage and self-love, a chance to reclaim those hidden parts of yourself that have been waiting for the light. There's a beautiful, authentic you waiting to be discovered in the shadows.

How Can Shadow Work Help?

I want you to imagine for a moment that you're trying to clean your room, but the lights are off. You stumble and trip over things, making little progress. To clean it thoroughly, you need to turn on the lights and see everything clearly. I mean true, actual spotlights shining into each and every corner of that room. You are finding things you haven't seen in years. The same principle applies to our inner world.

Shadow work is like turning on the lights in the room of your soul. It's about bringing to light those aspects of yourself that you've hidden away, often unconsciously. These hidden aspects, your "shadow," can include past traumas, unresolved emotions, and aspects of your personality you've deemed unacceptable. By shining a light on them, you can:

◆ **Heal:** Just as treating a wound requires cleaning it first, healing emotional wounds starts with acknowledging them. Shadow work helps you address and heal these emotional wounds.

◆ **Fully understand:** To understand yourself fully, you must explore every facet of your being, even the ones you've tucked away. In this life, we won't grow or heal if we only acknowledge the amazing things about ourselves. Shadow work provides you with the tools to do just that.

◆ **Improve:** Growth is impossible without self-awareness. Shadow work helps you become more aware of your patterns, triggers, and behaviors, enabling you to improve yourself and your life.

 ## Comparing the Pros and Cons of Shadow Work

Pros:

◆ **Personal growth:** Shadow work is a catalyst for profound personal growth, empowering you to become the best version of yourself.

◆ **Emotional liberation:** It frees you from the burden of repressed emotions, allowing you to experience emotional freedom. No more hiding behind those shadows.

◆ **Enhanced relationships:** As you better understand and heal yourself, your relationships can become healthier and more fulfilling.

Cons:

◆ **Emotional challenge:** Shadow work is emotionally challenging as you confront buried pain and emotions. We need to feel that pain before the light finds its way in.

◆ **Time-consuming:** It's a process that takes time and patience. Immediate results may not always be evident.

◆ **Requires self-compassion:** Self-compassion is essential because facing your shadows can trigger feelings of guilt or shame.

Dispelling common misconceptions about shadow work:

1 **It's only for "broken" people:** Shadow work is not just for those who are deeply wounded. It's a tool for anyone seeking personal growth and self-improvement.

2 **It's too dark and scary:** While it can be challenging, shadow work is a process of self-illumination, not darkness. It's about illuminating and bringing them a source of light.

3 **It's self-indulgent:** Shadow work is about self-awareness, not self-indulgence. It's a way to become a better person and improve your relationships.

4 **It's all about blame:** Shadow work is not about blaming yourself or others. It's about understanding and healing, not assigning blame.

5 **It's a one-time fix:** Shadow work is an ongoing process. It's not something you should expect to happen quickly but a healing journey of self-discovery and growth that lasts a lifetime.

Did you know that the word shadow work is trending on TikTok, with videos hitting 2.1 billion views and counting? Shadow work has gained TikTok traction, but we know it is nothing new. So, why the sudden gain in popularity? It is thought to have regained popularity because of a growing interest in overall self-awareness, holistic well-being, and personal growth (Mayer, 2023).

Be Mindful of the Triggers

We need to be mindful of why shadow work can be triggering. We also need to pay attention to how these emotional triggers are like neon lights pointing to areas in our lives that need our attention and care.

Let's begin by addressing a crucial aspect of shadow work—its potential to be triggering. When you start exploring your inner self, you might experience emotions and memories that you've long suppressed or ignored. This can feel uncomfortable and a bit scary at times. But remember, these emotional triggers are not obstacles; they are opportunities for healing.

- **Emotional triggers as neon lights:** Think of emotional triggers as red flags that signal unresolved issues within you. These triggers are like road signs, guiding you toward the areas in your life that need tender loving care. They point the way to hidden wounds that, once addressed, can lead to profound personal growth and emotional healing.

- **Keep track of your triggers:** As you continue down this path, keeping a journal or notebook handy is essential. Whenever you encounter an emotional trigger, take a moment to write it down. Describe the situation, your feelings, and any memories that surface. This will help you gain clarity on recurring patterns and themes in your life.

Exercise: Tracking Your Triggers

Let's dive into an exercise to help you identify and track your emotional triggers:

Step 1: Find a quiet and comfortable space where you won't be disturbed. Take a few deep breaths to center yourself.

Step 2: Below, notice the table with three columns: "Trigger," "Feelings," and "Memories."

Trigger	Feelings	Memories

Step 3: Whenever you encounter an emotional trigger in your daily life, write it down in the "Trigger" column. Be specific and honest about what triggered you.

Step 4: In the "Feelings" column, describe the emotions that arise when you're triggered. Are you angry, anxious, sad, or confused? Write it all down.

Step 5: In the "Memories" column, jot down any associated memories or past experiences that come to mind when you're triggered. These could be from your childhood, relationships, or other significant life events.

Step 6: After a week or two of tracking your triggers, take some time to review your entries. Notice any recurring patterns or themes. Are there specific triggers that keep resurfacing? Are there common feelings or memories associated with these triggers?

Step 7: Reflect on what you've discovered. What do these triggers tell you about yourself? How might they be connected to your past experiences or unresolved issues?

Remember, this exercise is about self-awareness, not judgment. It's a powerful tool to help you navigate your shadow with compassion and understanding. The more you become aware of your triggers, the better equipped you'll be to address them at your own pace.

I know we covered a lot of new territory and, at times, scary topics in this chapter. As I keep saying, we have to go into the dark before we find the light. It will be worth it you are worth it. In the next chapter, we will be leaning into our complete whole self. By becoming self-aware and acknowledging our suppressed emotions, limiting beliefs, and inner conflicts, we open the door to deep healing and personal growth. This chapter was meant to lay the foundation of shadow work, and now we will integrate our shadow self and uncover the hidden gems that reside within.

CHAPTER 2

SEEING THE SELF-
THE JOURNEY TO
SELF-ACCEPTANCE

Seeing the Self-
The Journey to Self-Acceptance

> *Your shadow is all of the things, 'positive' and 'negative,' that you've denied about yourself and hidden beneath the surface of the mask you forgot that you're wearing.* **–Oli Anderson**

If you're here, it means you've taken that courageous first step toward self-discovery and personal growth. I want you to know that I'm here to guide you through this process with compassion, understanding, and the utmost respect.

You may be feeling a mix of emotions right now—apprehension, curiosity, maybe even a bit of doubt. That's completely normal. Many of us, at some point in our lives, have felt like we're out of control, struggling to navigate the tumultuous sea of our own emotions. We've experienced anxiety, fear, guilt, sadness, exhaustion, and even depression. It's part of the human experience.

I want you to know that you have the power to regain control, to heal, and to find a path to emotional well-being. That's what shadow work is all about.

Seeing our entire being clearly helps us identify who we are, how we work best in life, and what we need to be successful. Imagine your self-awareness as a puzzle, and each piece of that puzzle represents a part of you. Some of those pieces may be shining in the light, while others are lurking in the shadows. The shadows are not something to be feared; they are simply parts of yourself that you haven't fully explored or accepted yet.

By obscuring part of our "picture," we limit our self-understanding and ability to grow and learn. Think of it as trying to drive a car with fogged-up windows— you can only see part of the road, and that's a recipe for accidents. Shadow work is like clearing away the fog so you can navigate your life with clarity and purpose.

In this chapter, we're going to explore practical tips and strategies to help you become more self-aware of the full self. You'll discover how to shine a light on those hidden parts of you so you can embrace them and use them to your advantage.

We'll also delve into relevant research and studies that support the concepts we discuss, giving you a solid foundation to understand why shadow work is so valuable. And, to make it all the more relatable, I'll share stories and case studies from real people who've embarked on their journey of self-discovery and transformation.

Remember, you have within you the potential for profound growth and healing. So, take a deep breath, let go of any apprehension, and let's start this transformative journey together. The destination? A more self-aware, self-accepting, and empowered you.

Are you ready? Let's begin.

Stories of Self-Awareness

The Lion Who Thought He Was a Sheep

Once upon a time, in a vast field, a lioness was nearing the end of her life. Tragically, she passed away shortly after giving birth to a cub. Confused and alone, the newborn lion cub found itself amidst a herd of sheep. A mother sheep took pity on the cub and decided to raise it as one of her own.

As the days turned into months, the lion cub grew up alongside the sheep. It adapted to their ways, bleating like a sheep and munching on grass. Yet, deep inside, it always felt like something was missing. The other sheep, in their ignorance, would often taunt the young lion, saying, "You're so odd! Your voice is strange. Why can't you be like the rest of us? You don't belong here!"

The lion endured the ridicule silently, feeling like it had betrayed the sheep community by being different. One day, an older lion from a distant jungle spotted the herd of sheep and decided to attack. Mid-chase, the older lion noticed the young lion running with the sheep.

Curiosity got the better of him, and he abandoned the chase, focusing on the younger lion instead. Pouncing on the cub, he growled, "Why are you running with these sheep?"

Terrified, the young lion stammered, "Please don't eat me! I'm just a sheep, I promise!"

The older lion, however, insisted, "That's not true! You are not a sheep; you are a lion, just like me."

The young lion repeated, "I'm a sheep please let me go."

The older lion had an idea. He dragged the young lion to a nearby river and urged it to look at its reflection. To its astonishment, the young lion saw its true self–a magnificent lion, not a sheep. Overwhelmed with joy, it roared mightily. The roar echoed through the jungle, frightening the sheep hiding in the bushes. They scattered, unable to mock or be near the lion anymore.

 ## *Moral of the Story*

The older lion represents self-awareness, and the reflection in the water symbolizes self-reflection. Just like the young lion, you may have grown up in a negative environment, absorbing limiting beliefs. But by looking inward, becoming self-aware, and challenging those beliefs, you can discover your true nature and align your life with it.

The older lion is not external but resides within you—it's your true self, your awareness. Let your awareness shine a light on your limiting beliefs, and you'll find your authentic self. Don't let past influences keep you stuck in your current reality; focus on self-discovery and growth.

Taming the Quick Temper

In a peaceful village, a young man approached a wise Zen master, seeking help for his uncontrollable anger. "My quick temper is ruining my relationships," he confessed.

The Zen master offered assistance, saying, "Can you show me your anger?"

The young man replied, "It happens suddenly; I can't demonstrate it right now."

The Zen master gently questioned, "If it's not present all the time, is it truly a part of your nature? Something that comes and goes isn't your true self, and you need not be defined by it."

The young man pondered this wisdom and left. As time passed, he began to observe his temper more closely. He gained control over it by bringing conscious awareness to it and repairing his damaged relationships.

 ## Moral of the Story

Your emotions don't define you, but they can control you if left unchecked. The path to taming subconscious reactions is to bring conscious awareness to them. Once you shine the light of consciousness on a belief, action, or emotion, it loses its power over you.

The Importance of Embracing the Light

So, why is it essential to embrace both the light and the shadow sides of ourselves? Let me explain with a real-life scenario:

Think of shadow work as a way to shed light on the hidden aspects of your inner world. The parts that often stay in the shadows are the emotions, thoughts, and experiences we've been told are wrong or unacceptable. For example, consider someone who firmly believes that feeling resentment as a father means they're ungrateful or a bad dad.

When this father has anger or frustration toward his child or a challenging situation in their life, they might react by ignoring or denying those feelings. They might even start thinking less of themselves because of these emotions. It's something many of us can relate to—feeling like we're not allowed to have certain feelings. "I better suppress this feeling, or I will be seen as this horrible dad."

These messages about what's acceptable and what's not come from various sources—our parents, relatives, teachers, and society at large. The problem is anything deemed "unacceptable" gets pushed into the shadow, hidden away from our conscious awareness.

By working on accepting and integrating these shadowed thoughts and emotions, we can experience greater internal peace. Instead of being driven unconsciously by our shadow self's hidden needs and feelings, we gain control over our reactions and emotions.

Embracing both the light and the shadow aspects of ourselves is an essential part of personal growth and self-awareness. Here's why we need it:

◆ **Wholeness and balance:** Each individual has positive and negative aspects of their personality, emotions, and experiences. Ignoring or repressing the shadow side can lead to an imbalance in your psyche. Embracing both sides allows you to become a more whole and balanced person.

◆ **Self-acceptance:** You can practice self-compassion and self-acceptance by acknowledging and accepting your shadow aspects. It's a way of saying, "I am human, and I have flaws and imperfections, but I am still deserving of love and respect."

◆ **Healing and growth:** Shadow work involves exploring your past wounds, traumas, fears, and negative patterns of behavior. By delving into these aspects of yourself, you can heal old wounds and grow as a person. It's a way to discover more about yourself and find ways to improve.

◆ **Improved relationships:** Understanding your own shadows can also help you better understand and navigate your interactions with others. It can lead to more empathetic and compassionate relationships because you're less likely to project your own unresolved issues onto others.

◆ **Increased self-awareness:** Shadow work fosters self-awareness by bringing unconscious patterns and behaviors to the surface. This awareness allows you to make conscious choices rather than reacting unconsciously to triggers from your shadow self.

◆ **Spiritual growth:** For some, embracing the shadow is a spiritual practice. It's seen as a path to enlightenment and self-realization, as it encourages self-examination and the pursuit of inner truth.

◆ **Creativity and authenticity:** Embracing your shadow can unlock hidden creative potentials and allow you to express yourself more authentically. Often, our most profound art, writing, and ideas come from our darkest and most vulnerable places.

So what happens if you never look into your shadows? That's a great question. Here are several things that can happen:

- **Unconscious patterns persist:** Unexamined shadows can continue to influence your behavior, often in destructive or self-sabotaging ways. You may repeatedly find yourself in unhealthy relationships or situations without understanding why.

- **Repression and denial:** Repressing your shadow aspects can lead to psychological and emotional problems. It's like sweeping issues under the rug instead of addressing them head-on.

- **Stagnation:** Without shadow work, personal growth and self-awareness can stagnate. You may miss out on opportunities for healing, transformation, and a deeper understanding of yourself.

- **Projection onto others:** Unresolved shadow aspects can lead to projecting your own negative qualities onto others. This can harm relationships and prevent you from taking responsibility for your own actions and feelings.

Embracing the light and the shadow of ourselves is key to personal growth, self-awareness, and overall well-being. It's a journey toward becoming a more balanced, authentic, and compassionate individual. Shadow work is a valuable tool in this process, helping you confront and integrate the hidden aspects of your psyche.

What Feeds Our Shadow Self?

Essentially, six key things feed our shadow self. Let's take a few moments and explore those more closely.

 ## *Avoidance*

Imagine you have a messy room in your house that you don't like to enter. You keep the door closed and avoid going in there because it's uncomfortable and chaotic. Similarly, avoidance in shadow work is when we dodge, ignore, or run away from parts of ourselves that make us uncomfortable. These can be feelings, memories, or thoughts we don't want to deal with. But guess what? The more we avoid them, the more they grow in the shadows.

 ## *Suppression*

Think of suppression like pushing a beachball underwater. You're using a lot of energy to keep it down, but eventually, it pops back up when you're not expecting it. In shadow work, suppression happens when we try to hide or bury parts of ourselves because we're afraid others won't accept them. This often comes from society's rules, like how we should behave, look, or think. We hide our true feelings and opinions to fit in, but this keeps our shadow self hidden and powerful.

 ## *Social Expectations and Suppression*

Imagine you're in a group of friends who all like a certain type of music. You might pretend to like that music too, even if you don't really enjoy it, just to fit in. This is because social norms and what our group considers normal can pressure us to hide our true preferences, opinions, or quirks. We suppress our uniqueness to belong.

Denial

Denial is like pretending that a big problem isn't there. It's like saying, "I'm not feeling sad at all," when you're actually bursting with sadness. In shadow work, denial is when we refuse to accept our flaws, mistakes, or negative feelings. We might say, "I'm always fine," even when we're hurting inside. Denial keeps us from recognizing and working on the parts of ourselves that need healing.

 ## *Guilt and Shame*

Imagine carrying around a heavy backpack filled with rocks. Guilt and shame are like those heavy rocks. Guilt is feeling bad about something you did, while shame is feeling like you're a bad person because of it. When we carry guilt and shame, we're feeding our shadow self. These emotions can make us hide our actions and emotions, trapping us in the shadows.

 ## *Fear*

Think of fear as a big, scary monster under your bed. It's the feeling that something bad will happen if you show your true self. Fear stops us from taking risks, expressing our needs, or being vulnerable. It's like a guard at the entrance to our shadow self, preventing us from exploring and understanding it.

Exercise: Getting to Know Your Shadow Self

Let's do a simple exercise to help you identify with your shadow self.

Find a quiet, comfortable, safe space.

Take a few deep breaths to relax.

Write down any memories, feelings, or thoughts you've been avoiding, suppressing, denying, feeling guilty or shameful about, or are afraid to face. Be honest with yourself. Remember, there's no judgment here; it's just you exploring your own feelings and experiences.

After you've done this, take 24 hours to reflect on what you've jotted down.

 Now, revisit what you wrote and reflect. Write down how they make you feel. Are you more comfortable with these emotions now than when you first wrote them? Can you feel a shift? These are the aspects of your shadow self, and acknowledging them is the first step to understanding and healing.

This exercise is like grabbing that flashing light and shining it into all those spaces in the attic and basement we've been avoiding. It may feel uncomfortable at first, but it's the beginning of your journey to embrace and befriend your shadow self. Remember, you're not alone in this, and you have the power to bring light to your shadows for personal growth and healing.

Embracing Our Whole Self

Before we dive into the "how," let's explore the "why." Why is it essential to embrace all facets of yourself, even the ones deemed to be lurking in the shadows? Well, here's the truth: we are complex beings, a kaleidoscope of experiences, emotions, and memories. Ignoring or suppressing parts of ourselves can lead to a whirlwind of unwanted feelings like anxiety, fear, guilt, sadness, and even depression.

Think of your shadow self as the unsung hero of your story. These hidden aspects hold the key to your growth, resilience, and healing. By acknowledging and accepting them, you not only free yourself from their grip but also pave the way for a more balanced, authentic, and joyful life.

 ### How to Accept Ourselves

Acceptance is a big deal in shadow work. It is easy to love and accept all the ooey, gooey pieces of ourselves. Learning to accept each and every detail is how we find absolute peace and growth. Let's review a few ways to find acceptance with our whole self.

Practice Self-Compassion

Begin by treating yourself with the same kindness and understanding you'd offer a dear friend. Recognize that you're human and that making mistakes is a part of life.

 ## Journal Your Thoughts

Feel free to use the space below to jot down your thoughts and feelings. This can help you gain clarity about your emotions and enable you to observe them from a more detached perspective. What should you focus on? Great question. I went ahead and added journal prompts to help.

 List at least five strengths, talents, or qualities you appreciate about yourself. How have these strengths positively impacted your life?

Your Strengths & Talents	Impact on Your Life
1. _____	1. _____
2. _____	2. _____
3. _____	3. _____
4. _____	4. _____
5. _____	5. _____

Write down a few of your perceived flaws or imperfections. Now, challenge yourself to see if there's a positive aspect or hidden strength within each of them.

Perceived Flaws	Hidden Strengths Within Your Flaws
1. _____	1. _____
2. _____	2. _____
3. _____	3. _____
4. _____	4. _____
5. _____	5. _____

Describe a recent situation where you were hard on yourself. How could you have shown more self-compassion in that moment? What would you say to a friend who was in a similar situation?

_____
_____
_____
_____
_____

Reflect on a mistake or regret from your past that you struggle to accept. Write about what you've learned from that experience and how it has shaped you.

_____

_____

_____

_____

_____

_____

Imagine a version of yourself who is unconditionally loved and accepted just as they are. Describe this version of yourself in detail. What would change in your life if you treated yourself with such love and acceptance?

_____

_____

_____

_____

_____

_____

Identify and describe your inner critic—the voice inside that judges and criticizes you. What triggers your inner critic, and how can you respond to it with kindness and understanding?

_____

_____

_____

_____

_____

What are some specific actions or steps you can take to practice self-acceptance daily? Set achievable goals for yourself.

1. _____
2. _____
3. _____
4. _____
5. _____
6. _____
7. _____
8. _____

Think of someone you admire and believe embodies self-acceptance. What qualities or behaviors do they exhibit that you could incorporate into your own life?

1. _____
2. _____
3. _____
4. _____
5. _____
6. _____
7. _____
8. _____

Write a letter to your future self, expressing your hopes for continued growth, self-acceptance, and self-love. What advice would you give your future self?

Date: -   -

_____,

_____

_____

_____

_____

_____

_____

_____

_____

_____

_____

_____

_____

_____

_____

_____

_____

_____

_____

_____

_____

How to Forgive Ourselves

Forgiving ourselves can be challenging, especially when we carry the weight of past mistakes. But remember, forgiving doesn't mean condoning the actions; it means releasing yourself from their grip. Try this forgiveness exercise:

 ### *Exercise: Letter to Yourself*

Find a quiet space where you won't be disturbed.

 Use the space below to write a letter to yourself, addressing the issue or mistake you want to forgive. Express your feelings honestly. Share your pain, anger, or disappointment.

_____,

_____

_____

_____

_____

_____

_____

_____

_____

_____

Now, shift your focus toward self-compassion. Remind yourself that you are human and humans make mistakes. It's a part of our journey.

In the space below, write a forgiveness statement: "I forgive myself for [specific mistake]. I release myself from its burden." Close the letter with words of self-love and acceptance.

I forgive myself for
_____
_____
_____
_____
_____

I release myself from it's burden and
_____
_____
_____
_____
_____
_____

Read this letter to yourself aloud. Feel the weight lifting as you say those forgiving words.

Embracing all parts of yourself, even the shadowy ones, is a powerful step toward healing and living a more fulfilled life. Keep going, and know that you're not alone on this path.

Exercise: Exploring Your Emotional Patterns

 List the emotions you experience most frequently (e.g., anxiety, fear, guilt). Now, next to each emotion, write down situations or triggers that typically evoke these feelings.

Emotions	What Evoked that Emotion?
1. _____	1. _____
2. _____	2. _____
3. _____	3. _____
4. _____	4. _____
5. _____	5. _____

Reflect on any recurring themes or patterns you notice. Is there a common thread connecting these emotions?

_____
_____
_____
_____
_____

Ask yourself why you feel this way in those situations. What beliefs or past experiences might be contributing to these emotions?

_____
_____
_____
_____
_____
_____

Don't judge yourself during this activity. The goal is simply to become more aware of your emotional landscape.

Mindfulness Is the Key

Mindfulness is a powerful tool in the realm of shadow work. It helps us transcend the ego, uncover our shadows, and heal from past traumas, all while getting in touch with our true selves. Let's explore mindfulness for self-awareness and ways to incorporate it into your daily life.

Mindfulness is a wonderful tool that lets us observe our thoughts, physical sensations, and emotions without judgment. This non-judgmental awareness is vital in shadow work because it helps us uncover hidden aspects of ourselves. When we're mindful, we can explore our shadow without being overwhelmed by it or reacting defensively.

How to Be More Mindful

- **Meditation:** It's like going to the gym for your mind. It strengthens your ability to be present and aware. It's a cornerstone of mindfulness because it teaches you to observe your thoughts and feelings without attachment. There are three types of meditation:

  - ◊ **Breathing and counting:** Find a quiet space, sit comfortably, and focus on your breath. Inhale deeply, counting to four, then exhale, counting to four. When your mind wanders (and it will), gently bring your attention back to your breath.

  - ◊ **Body scan:** Lie down or sit comfortably and bring your attention to different parts of your body, starting from your toes and moving up to your head. Be mindful of any sensations or feelings without trying to change them.

  - ◊ **Walking meditation:** Take a slow, deliberate walk. Pay attention to the sensation of your feet lifting, moving, and landing. Feel the ground beneath you with each step.

- **Using your senses:** Take a moment to pause during your day and engage your senses. For example, while having a meal, really taste the flavors, smell the aromas, and feel the textures. Doing this will help keep you present.

- **Notice your thoughts and feelings:** Imagine your thoughts and feelings as clouds passing by in the sky. Instead of getting carried away by them, stand back and observe them. Ask yourself, "What am I thinking and feeling right now?" without judgment.

How to Include Mindfulness in Your Daily Life

Okay, so we now know that being mindful is important, but as busy as we are, how can we possibly fit it into our day? Below, you will find some helpful suggestions to do just that:

♦ **Morning routine:** Start your day with a short mindfulness practice, even if it's just a few minutes of deep breathing or a quick body scan.

♦ **Mindful breaks:** Take short mindfulness breaks throughout the day. Set reminders on your phone to pause, breathe deeply, and notice your surroundings.

♦ **Mindful eating:** You can achieve this by enjoying each bite before swallowing. Focus on those amazing flavors in your mouth. Put away distractions like phones or TV and fully engage with your meal.

♦ **Mindful walking:** Incorporate mindfulness into your daily walks. Pay attention to the rhythm of your steps and the world around you.

Now, whenever you need an instant dose of mindfulness, simply:

♦ **Pause:** Simply pause what you're doing.

♦ **Breathe:** Take a few deep breaths to center yourself.

♦ **Observe:** Notice your thoughts, emotions, and physical sensations in the moment.

Remember, mindfulness is a skill that improves with practice. Be patient with yourself and approach it with an open heart. Over time, it will become an essential tool in your shadow work journey, helping you connect with your true self and heal from past wounds.

In this chapter, we've explored the profound power of mindfulness in peeling back the layers of your true self, moving beyond the ego, shadow, and trauma. You've learned that by being mindful, you can observe your thoughts, feelings, and sensations without judgment, creating a deeper connection with your authentic self.

In the upcoming chapter, you will check out practical guidance, exercises, and safety measures to ensure that you embark on this path with confidence and care. I understand that this can be a vulnerable process, and your well-being is always the utmost priority. So, get ready to explore your inner world further, heal old wounds, and discover the incredible potential that lies within you.

CHAPTER 3
SAFE INWARD
JOURNEYS

❖

Safe Inward Journeys

> It is only through shadows that one comes to know the light. *–St. Catherine of Siena*

During this chapter, I want to spend some time examining the essential art of creating safe spaces within ourselves for the profound work that lies ahead. If you're new to shadow work, you might be feeling a mix of curiosity and apprehension.

We'll explore the importance of safety in the inward journey. Just as an explorer prepares for an expedition with the right gear and knowledge, we must prepare ourselves for the expedition into our inner world. I want to equip you with the tools, techniques, and understanding needed to ensure your journey is as safe and nurturing as possible.

Before we dive into practical tips and transformative activities, let's address why this chapter is so important.

You may have noticed that you're experiencing a range of challenging emotions–anxiety, fear, guilt, sadness, and exhaustion. You might even be dealing with depression. These feelings are signs that you're carrying a heavy emotional burden, a part of which is hidden in your shadow self. It's natural to want to explore and heal these wounds, but doing so without proper preparation can sometimes lead to emotional overwhelm.

Think of shadow work as an archeological dig into the depths of your psyche. As you unearth long-buried emotions and beliefs, you might encounter treasures of self-awareness, but you might also stumble upon hidden pain and trauma. That's why it's crucial to create a safe environment within yourself–a sanctuary where you can explore without feeling overwhelmed or unsafe.

What to Expect in This Chapter

- **Practical tips and strategies:** I'll provide you with easy-to-follow guidelines on how to establish a personal, mental, and emotional safe space. These strategies will help you navigate the often challenging terrain of your inner world.

- **Workbook activities:** Throughout this chapter, you'll find interactive exercises designed to help you apply the concepts we discuss. These activities are like the tools you'll need for your inward journey, helping you dig deeper and uncover the hidden gems within your shadow self.

- **Research and studies:** I'll present you with insights from psychological research and studies related to self-guided therapy and shadow work. This knowledge will give you a solid foundation as you embark on your exploration.

- **Relatable stories:** To remind you that you're not alone on this journey, I'll share stories and case studies of individuals who have walked a similar path. These stories will provide inspiration and show you that transformation is possible.

As we move forward, remember that shadow work is a profound act of self-love and personal growth. The road may be challenging, but it's also incredibly rewarding. Our goal is to create a safe and inviting space for you to explore your inner world, gain self-understanding, and embark on a healing journey that can transform your life.

So, let's begin. Let's be safe, compassionate, and resilient!

Morgan's Story

Morgan had carried the weight of anxiety and self-doubt for as long as she could remember. She often found herself stuck in a cycle of self-criticism, unable to break free from the grip of her inner demons. One day, while browsing through a local bookstore, she stumbled upon a book about shadow work. It was a serendipitous moment, one that would change the course of her life.

Morgan's anxiety was like a persistent shadow, always lurking in the background. It kept her from pursuing her dreams, forming meaningful connections, and feeling at ease in her own skin. She knew she needed to confront these inner demons to find true happiness and fulfillment.

With a mix of apprehension and determination, Morgan decided to delve into the world of shadow work. She began by setting aside a small corner of her cozy apartment, a safe space for her journey of self-discovery. Armed with a journal and a commitment to herself, she started writing down her thoughts and feelings.

Each evening, Morgan would sit in her favorite armchair, pen in hand, and pour her heart onto the pages of her journal. She wrote about her fears, her past traumas, and her insecurities. At first, it was painful to confront these aspects of herself, but gradually, she began to see patterns emerge. The act of writing allowed her to distance herself from her emotions to observe them from a more objective standpoint.

In addition to journaling, Morgan embraced meditation as a way to quiet her racing thoughts. She would sit on her balcony, surrounded by the gentle rustling of leaves, and focus on her breath. This practice brought her a newfound sense of calm and allowed her to connect with her inner self.

Recognizing the importance of community, Morgan sought out support groups for people on their own shadow work journeys. Here, she found kindred spirits who shared their stories and provided guidance. Being part of a group gave her a sense of belonging and reassurance that she wasn't alone in her struggles.

As Morgan continued her self-guided self-help journey, she experienced moments of breakthrough and liberation. She uncovered the root causes of her anxiety and self-doubt, often tied to childhood experiences and societal pressures. Understanding these origins was like turning on a light in the darkness of her mind.

Yet, there came a time when Morgan's anxiety became overwhelming. It was during a particularly challenging week when she decided to take a step further. She reached out to those she trusted; she didn't try to go it alone. She also was mindful of those times when she would need to lean on her therapist. Understanding that took a burden off her own shoulders. She felt more comfortable continuing her work, knowing the help was there when and if she needed it.

Morgan combined the insights she gained from self-help with the expertise of her therapist. Together, they created a well-rounded approach to her healing journey. Morgan continued her journaling and meditation.

Morgan's journey was messy and wonderful, and it was also transformative. Over time, her anxiety and self-doubt gradually loosened their grip on her. She learned to be kinder to herself, to accept her imperfections, and to embrace her shadow as an integral part of who she was.

Morgan's story is a testament to the power of self-guided self-help, combined with the wisdom of professional guidance when needed. It's proof that, with courage and commitment, anyone can embark on a journey of self-discovery, healing, and personal growth. Morgan's life transformed, and yours can, too, as you venture into your own shadow work journey.

Remember, you have the power within you to explore and heal your shadow self. Self-guided self-help is a valuable tool to get you started on this path, but don't hesitate to seek professional help when needed.

Exercise: Journaling for Insecurities

I want to take a pause here and ask you to do some shadow work. In the space below, I would like you to do some journaling. Much like in Morgan's story above, journaling can help you focus on your insecurities, fears, and past trauma.

Before diving into these questions, remember that shadow work can be emotionally challenging. Find a time when you have solitude and can devote your full attention to these reflections. Feel free to select and modify the prompts that resonate most with you and answer those for the most effective results.

> I want you to remember your childhood hero. Think of them now; what image comes to mind?

_____

_____

_____

_____

> When was the first time you felt insecure as a child? Do you remember what triggered this feeling?

_____

_____

_____

> As a child, when did you first feel let down? Write down as many details surrounding the circumstances. Do you feel this affected your ability to accept help and love? How?

_____

_____

_____

_____

 Recall your parents' or guardians' beliefs during your childhood. Are your current beliefs aligned with theirs? How are you different? How are you the same?

_____

_____

_____

 Think back to beliefs you were made to follow in your childhood that you now resent as an adult. Do these influence your behavior today? How?

_____

_____

_____

 When you find yourself feeling insecure, do you participate in self-sabotaging actions? If so, which ones?

1. _____

2. _____

3. _____

4. _____

5. _____

Can you think of any beliefs from your childhood that contribute to your insecurity? For instance, thoughts like "This is too difficult" or "I'm not good enough."

1. _____
_____

2. _____
_____

3. _____
_____

4. _____
_____

5. _____
_____

Do you think your insecurities hold you back? If so, explain how.

_____
_____
_____
_____
_____
_____
_____
_____

How do social media, parental pressures, or even cultural expectations cause insecurity in you?

_____
_____
_____
_____
_____

_____

_____

_____

_____

_____

> **Do you have difficulty not comparing yourself to others? Why do you think you do this?**

_____

_____

_____

_____

_____

_____

_____

_____

Take your time with these questions, and remember that the process is about self-discovery and growth. Embrace each insight as a step toward a more profound understanding of yourself and your journey toward healing and personal development.

Can You Really Be Your Own Therapist?

While professional therapy has its benefits, self-guided self-help is a fantastic complement or even a starting point, especially if you're on a budget or want to explore your inner world at your own pace.

I want to emphasize that self-guided self-help is not a replacement for professional therapy, especially if you're dealing with severe emotional issues. However, it can be a powerful supplement to your healing journey. Here are some tips on how to effectively become your own self-therapist:

- **Read and research widely:**
  Educate yourself about shadow work, self-awareness, and personal growth. Books, articles, and online resources can provide valuable insights and guidance.

- **Attend workshops and support groups:**
  If possible, participate in local workshops or online support groups. Connecting with others on a similar journey can be incredibly enriching.

- **One thing at a time:**
  Avoid overwhelming yourself by trying to tackle all your issues simultaneously. Choose one aspect of your shadow self to focus on at a time.

- **Journal, but don't ruminate:**
  Give yourself time each day for journaling and self-reflection. This helps you process your thoughts and emotions without dwelling on them throughout the day.

- **Get other perspectives:**
  Seek out trusted friends, mentors, or support groups to gain different viewpoints on your challenges. An outside perspective often provides clarity.

- **Use talk as therapy with a trusted mentor or friend:**
  Engage in open and honest conversations with someone you trust. Sharing your feelings and thoughts can be therapeutic in itself.

- **Be mindful:**
  Mindfulness practices, such as meditation and deep breathing, can help you become more aware of your emotions and reactions.

◆ **Do check in with a counselor, mentor, life coach, or friend if needed:**
Recognize when self-help isn't enough. If your emotions become too overwhelming or if you feel stuck, it's perfectly okay to seek professional guidance.

Studies have shown that people who actively engage in self-help practices often experience improved emotional regulation, increased self-awareness, and enhanced overall well-being (Ackerman, 2019). While self-help is a valuable tool, it's essential to remember that it may not be sufficient for everyone, particularly those with complex emotional challenges.

The Affordability and Accessibility of Self-Guided Therapy

We need to address the elephant in the room—the affordability and accessibility of therapy. It's a very real issue that many people face, and it can indeed create anxiety and uncertainty.

So, picture this: a recent survey of 1000 adults in therapy across America came up with some interesting findings. Nearly 40% of the folks in the survey had to reach out for some financial assistance just to make it to their therapy sessions. Among the survey participants, a majority (that's 62%) mentioned that they had to dig into their own pockets for some therapy expenses. On average, that came up to about $178 a month, even though a whopping 71% said they had some insurance coverage, and 36% were getting a hand from Employee Assistance Programs (EAP) to help with the costs (Ingram, 2022).

Now, here's where it gets real. A significant chunk, about 38%, needed some financial support from someone else just to keep up with therapy. And for some, the financial strain was so heavy that they had to hit pause on their therapy sessions. Roughly a third had to cancel appointments because of those out-of-pocket costs, 39% cut back on the frequency of their sessions to save some cash, and 31% temporarily stopped therapy to manage bigger expenses. Over 1 in 3 Americans surveyed who are no longer in therapy shared that they had to quit because of cost-related reasons (Ingram, 2022).

So, you see, the need for therapy is on the rise, but the worry about being able to afford it isn't going away. This is where self-guided therapy steps in as an accessible and cost-effective option to help you on your journey to personal growth and healing.

Let's break down why self-guided therapy can be beneficial:

◆ **Cost-effective:** Self-guided therapy is budget-friendly. In fact, it's often significantly more affordable than traditional therapy sessions. You won't have to worry about recurring out-of-pocket expenses, like co-pays or monthly fees. You can access self-guided resources for a fraction of the cost and sometimes even for free.

◆ **No insurance hassles:** You won't have to navigate the complexities of insurance coverage or worry about insurance changes affecting your access to therapy. Self-guided therapy puts you in control of your healing journey without financial constraints.

◆ **Flexible schedule:** Self-guided therapy allows you to work at your own pace and on your own schedule. This flexibility is especially beneficial if you have a busy life or commitments that make it challenging to attend regular therapy appointments.

◆ **Privacy and comfort:** You get to create a safe and inviting space for yourself to explore your shadow self. There's no need to share your innermost thoughts and feelings with a stranger. Self-guided therapy allows you to reflect and grow in the comfort of your own space.

◆ **Consistent progress:** With self-guided therapy, you can maintain a consistent practice without worrying about financial setbacks. This consistency can lead to more significant personal growth and self-healing over time.

◆ **Evidence-based approaches:** Self-guided therapy often incorporates research-based strategies and techniques, ensuring that you receive effective guidance in your journey toward self-awareness and healing.

We love and value therapists. The work they do is invaluable, and there are specific roles they play in the mental health field. It is essential to understand that. It is also important to know what role you can play in your mental health journey.

Self-guided therapy provides an affordable, accessible, and effective way to explore your shadow self, regulate your emotions, and experience personal growth. It's a valuable option to consider on your path to self-healing, offering you the tools and resources to take control of your emotional well-being without the financial burden.

Tracking Your Progress

I know that shadow work can be a challenging yet profoundly rewarding endeavor. As you embark on this path toward understanding your shadow self, tracking your progress is an essential compass guiding you through the twists and turns of your inner landscape. Here, I'll provide you with practical tips and exercises to help you do just that.

 Exercise: Journaling Your Progress

I recommend the tactile approach of writing down your answers as it engages a different part of your brain, fostering deeper reflection and growth. Now, let's get started:

Before diving into shadow work, take a moment to reflect on where you are right now. Write down your current emotional state, thoughts, and any specific challenges you're facing. Be honest with yourself; this is your starting point, your reference for measuring progress.

 Establishing achievable goals is like setting the destination on your GPS for this journey. What are you looking to achieve through shadow work? Write down your goals, needs, and desires. Remember, effective goals should be specific, measurable, achievable, and flexible. For instance, if you're working on why certain people trigger you, your goal could be to be kinder and more respectful to people, regardless of who they are.

Tracking your progress involves understanding your emotional landscape. Create a daily routine where you check in with your feelings. Use a simple chart to jot down how you're feeling when you wake up, and note if it changes throughout the day. Ask yourself why your emotions fluctuate. If something significant happens during the day that affects your feelings, make a note of it.

Here's a sample chart:

DAY 1	
Morning Emotion: _____	Evening Emotion: _____
What changed today: _____	

DAY 2

Morning Emotion: _____

_____
_____
_____
_____

Evening Emotion: _____

_____
_____
_____
_____

What changed today: _____

_____
_____
_____
_____
_____
_____

DAY 3

Morning Emotion: _____

_____
_____
_____
_____

Evening Emotion: _____

_____
_____
_____
_____

What changed today: _____

_____
_____
_____
_____
_____
_____

Throughout your journey, pay close attention to any shifts or changes in how you feel. Write them down. Are you noticing improvements in your mood, confidence, or overall outlook on life? Conversely, are there recurring themes or triggers that still cause you distress? Actively recognizing these changes will help tailor your shadow work plan to meet your evolving needs.

List Your Improvements	Triggers Still Causing You Distress

Remember that progress takes various forms. It might be a sense of relief after a challenging session, feeling more in control of your emotions, or witnessing changes in your behavior and thought patterns. These changes may be subtle, so keep an eye out for them.

Sometimes, those close to us can spot our progress before we do. Don't hesitate to seek feedback and insight from trusted friends, family members, or support groups. Their external perspective can provide a more comprehensive picture of your growth.

Maintain open and honest communication with yourself. This is key to tracking your progress. Write down your experiences, challenges, and victories openly and regularly. Be open; nobody else will read this. This practice will help you monitor your progress over time and identify any challenges hindering your growth. Even when facing setbacks, be honest with yourself and record them. Setbacks are part of the journey, not a roadblock.

Lastly, consider keeping a dedicated journal or note-taking app for your shadow work. This will serve as a valuable reference for reflecting on your progress. Jot down your thoughts, emotions, breakthroughs, and setbacks. It's like keeping a diary of your inner transformation, and it can help you stay organized and gain insights into your journey.

Remember, tracking your progress is not about judgment; it's about self-discovery and growth. Celebrate each and every one of your successes, and acknowledge your challenges as stepping stones toward a better you. With each step, you're closer to understanding and owning your shadow self.

What If I Need Help?

Rest assured that there is a good chance you will. I don't say this to frighten you but only to prepare you. Laying all the cards on the table allows one to know what to expect and educate themselves. So, when the time comes, and you feel that overwhelming need for backup, what should you do?

First, I want to remind you to take your time. It is far too common in traditional therapy that we complain about how long it is taking. That is for a reason. If we rush certain processes, we can do more harm than good. Take your time, and progress at a pace that feels comfortable for you. If you feel overwhelmed or like you're moving too quickly, it's okay to slow down. This is your journey, and you must honor your timing.

Have a Support Shadow Work Buddy

Now, let's say you are going about your process at a reasonable pace, yet you still feel those feelings of anxiety or fear rushing in. It can be incredibly beneficial to have a partner or friend who is also on a path of self-discovery. This person can be your sounding board, someone to bounce ideas off of, and a source of encouragement when things get tough. Together, you can share your experiences, learn from each other, and provide emotional support during challenging moments.

Use Self-Calming and Self-Soothing Techniques

There will be times when you encounter intense emotions or challenging aspects of yourself during shadow work. During these moments, it's crucial to have tools at your disposal to calm and soothe yourself. Here are some techniques to try:

Grounding Exercises

◆ **5-4-3-2-1 grounding:** This is a common exercise to keep you present and calm. Start with calling out five things you can physically see. Then, move on to four things you can actually touch. Next are three things you can hear and two things you can smell in the air. Last, you want to focus on one thing you can taste, for instance, maybe that lingering coffee you just had. This exercise helps bring you back to the present moment.

- **Rooted visualization:** Imagine yourself as a tree with deep roots firmly planted in the earth. Feel the stability and support of the ground beneath you.

- **Deep breathing:** Take slow, deep breaths, focusing on the sensation of your breath moving in and out. This helps calm your nervous system.

- **Body scan:** Mentally scan your body, starting from your toes and moving up to your head. Pay attention to any areas of tension and consciously release it.

- **Nature connection:** Spend time in nature, whether it's a walk in the park or sitting in your backyard. Nature has a calming effect on our emotions.

 ## Calming Exercises

- **Progressive muscle relaxation:** For this exercise, you are going to start at the very top of your head and work down to your toes. Working one muscle group at a time, you want to tense that muscle group, for instance, your shoulders, and then relax.

- **Visualization:** Take a moment and picture yourself in a calm and safe place. Visualize the details, such as colors, sounds, and smells, to create a sense of calm.

- **Mindfulness meditation:** Practice mindfulness by focusing on your breath and observing your thoughts without judgment. The purpose of this is to help you stay focused and reduce anxiety.

- **Affirmations:** Use positive affirmations to counteract negative thoughts and emotions. Repeat phrases like, "I am safe" or "I am in control of my emotions."

- **Aromatherapy:** Aromatherapy with calming scents like lavender or chamomile can help relax your mind and body.

Only Do What Feels Slightly Uncomfortable

As you dive into your shadow work, it's important to challenge yourself, but not to the point of overwhelming discomfort. Aim to explore areas that are slightly uncomfortable, where you can grow without feeling entirely overwhelmed. This gradual approach allows for sustainable progress. A good rule of thumb is don't do more than 20% uncomfortable.

Safe Space Exercises

Begin by taking a deep breath and finding a comfortable position.

If you feel safe, gently close your eyes.

Be mindful of your breath.

Can you feel the rise and fall of your chest?

Observe the sensation as you inhale.

And notice how it feels as you exhale.

It's natural to be distracted by other thoughts or sounds that may come into your awareness.

That's perfectly okay.

Acknowledge these thoughts and sounds, and then let them drift away.

Return your attention to your breathing, recognizing how it ushers in calmness and stillness into your being.

Now, picture yourself in a unique place—a place where you experience safety, tranquility, and freedom.

This is a place brimming with serenity and delight.

Perhaps it's a location you've visited in the past, or maybe it's a place you're crafting with your imagination.

Take a moment to explore—what captures your attention?

What sights do you see, and what colors stand out?

What sounds surround you?

Is there a particular scent in the air?

Picture yourself in this sanctuary of yours.

What activities are you engaged in?

Feel the sense of calm and resilience washing over you as you recall your own strengths, skills, and unique qualities.

Before departing from your haven, take a final glance around and notice any other details that come into focus.

Remember, this is a special sanctuary that resides within you, a place you can revisit whenever you wish.

Each time you return, it serves as a reminder of your inner strength and the unique qualities that make you who you are.

Now, gently shift your attention back to your breath.

When you're ready, you may choose to open your eyes, carrying with you the feelings of tranquility and resilience.

Trigger Exercise

 ### *Step 1: Recognize Your Emotional Triggers*

The initial stage in effectively handling your emotional reactions is recognizing what triggers them. These triggers can encompass a wide range of things, including specific situations, events, or thoughts that evoke strong emotional responses within you. Examples of triggers may encompass scenarios like public speaking, criticism, financial challenges, or feelings of rejection.

 To identify your personal triggers, take some time for self-reflection. Think back to your past experiences and recall situations or events that have ignited intense emotional reactions within you. Jot down instances that provoke strong emotions for you.

1. _____

_____

2. _____

_____

3. _____

_____

4. _____

_____

5. _____

_____

Step 2: Describe Your Emotional Response

Once you've pinpointed your triggers, it's important to contemplate how you typically react when these triggers manifest in your life. This introspection can provide valuable insights into the impact these triggers have on your emotional well-being.

 Reactions can vary widely and may encompass emotions such as anxiety, anger, or sadness. You might also notice physical reactions like trembling or perspiration. Honesty with yourself during this self-assessment is essential, as it will aid in identifying the most effective coping strategies for you. Write down your reactions.

1. _____
2. _____
3. _____
4. _____
5. _____

Step 3: Cultivate Effective Coping Strategies

The final phase involves the development of coping strategies designed to manage your emotional responses when faced with triggers. Coping strategies can encompass a diverse array of techniques. As we discussed, this can include deep breathing exercises, mindfulness meditation, or practicing positive self-talk.

Selecting coping strategies that resonate with you and align with your comfort level is of paramount importance. Additionally, don't hesitate to experiment with various strategies to discover what works best for different situations. By cultivating these coping mechanisms, you empower yourself to regulate your emotional responses and diminish the impact that triggers have on your life.

In this chapter, we took a closer look at how to approach self-guided therapy and shadow work with safety and mindfulness. We explored various practical strategies and techniques to ensure that as you immerse yourself in the depths of your inner world, you do so with care and self-compassion.

Keep in mind that your path toward self-healing and personal growth is profound and filled with transformative moments. It's perfectly normal to have questions, concerns, and moments of apprehension as you move forward. We've equipped you with the tools to establish a secure and welcoming space for your personal development, including setting boundaries, recognizing your triggers, and crafting coping strategies.

In the forthcoming chapter, we will closely examine the beginning steps of shadow work. We'll uncover how to illuminate those concealed aspects of yourself and commence the journey of self-discovery. As you move ahead, have confidence in your ability to navigate the shadows and embrace the light that awaits you.

The exploration continues, and the potential for growth and self-understanding is boundless. So, turn the page with assurance, for the next chapter holds the key to unlocking your inner potential and uncovering the transformative essence of shadow work.

CHAPTER 4
SETTING FOOT ON THE SHADOW PATH

Setting Foot on the Shadow Path

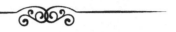

> **"** *Our shadows hold the essence of who we are. They hold our most treasured gifts. By facing these aspects of ourselves, we become free to experience our glorious totality: the good and the bad, the dark and the light.* **–Debbie Ford**

My goal in this chapter is to provide you with simple yet effective strategies and methods to embark on your shadow work journey.

I want to emphasize that shadow work doesn't have to be overwhelming. In fact, we'll begin with simple, manageable steps designed with beginners like you in mind. My goal is to make this process as easy to understand and approach as possible. Remember, it's not about rushing through the work; it's about progressing at your own pace.

This is a space for optimism and growth, and I believe in your ability to make transformative changes in your life. You've already taken the first step by opening this workbook, and that's something to be proud of.

Are you ready to start on this journey of self-discovery and healing? Let's start by hearing Sebastian's story.

Sebastian had always been a man of grit and determination. His life's mission was to banish the word "wimp" from his vocabulary, a word that had haunted him since he was just five years old. It was a sunny afternoon when he and his father had taken a stroll in the park. Sebastian was a bundle of energy, but when he saw the pony ride, fear gripped his little heart. His father, a stern and imposing figure, looked down at him with a disapproving scowl.

"What kind of man are you going to make?" his father barked. "You're nothing but a little wimp, you're an embarrassment in our family."

Those words etched themselves into Sebastian's psyche, shaping the man he would become. From that day forward, he resolved to obliterate any trace of weakness within him.

As the years passed, Sebastian dedicated himself to the pursuit of strength and toughness, ignoring an entire part of his being. He became a black belt in karate, sculpted his body with weightlifting, and was always the first to volunteer for challenging tasks. He despised weakness, not only in himself but in others as well. He saw vulnerability as a character flaw, something to be eradicated at all costs.

Yet, despite all his efforts, he found himself haunted by moments when he felt like that little boy on the pony ride. There were times when he had to admit that he was still, in some areas of his life, a "wimp." It was in those moments that he had a strange revelation. Being a wimp had its advantages. It made him cautious, which kept him out of fights and, during his college years, prevented him from going out with friends when he knew heavy alcohol use was involved. This caution saved him from a tragic accident that claimed the life of his closest friend and severely injured others.

It was this life-altering event that prompted Sebastian to pause and reflect on the path he had been on. He had tried so hard to hide his weakness, to prove his worth to the world, that he had become someone he didn't even recognize. He chased dreams he didn't truly desire, filling his days with empty duties that left him feeling hollow.

One day, while watching a colleague struggle with a task at work, Sebastian muttered to himself, "He's such a wimp, and I hate wimps." But as the words escaped his lips, he felt a strange pang of self-awareness. He realized that his strong aversion to weakness in others was a reflection of his own neglect of his shadow self. It was a projection of his inner struggle to be perfect, to never show vulnerability or imperfection.

That moment of self-realization marked the beginning of Sebastian's journey into the depths of his own psyche. He decided to confront the shadows he had long buried within himself. He began to explore his own vulnerabilities, acknowledging that they were not signs of weakness but of his humanity.

Sebastian started to explore his shadow self. Through introspection and guided self-discovery, he unearthed buried emotions and confronted long-held beliefs about masculinity and strength. He learned that true strength didn't come from denying his vulnerabilities but from embracing them.

Over time, Sebastian transformed from a man obsessed with proving his toughness to one who understood the power of vulnerability and compassion. He repaired broken relationships and forged deeper connections with those around him. He no longer saw weakness in others as something to despise but as an opportunity for growth and understanding.

Sebastian's journey into his shadow self was not easy, but it was necessary for his personal growth and well-being. He discovered that accepting and integrating his "wimpish" tendencies allowed him to become a more authentic and empathetic person. In the end, he found that true strength was not in the absence of weakness but in the courage to confront and embrace it.

How to Spot Your Inner Shadow

In this part of your shadow work journey, we'll explore practical tips, exercises, and insights to help you identify and understand the hidden aspects of yourself that might be causing emotional turmoil. Remember, this is a safe and supportive space for you to grow and heal.

Triggers

Triggers are powerful messengers from your inner shadow, and they can be our best teachers if we pay attention to them. Here's a simple exercise to help you spot your triggers.

 ### *Exercise: Trigger Journal*

 Over the next week, whenever you feel emotionally charged—whether it's anger, frustration, sadness, or anxiety—write down the situation, the emotions you felt, and your immediate reactions.

Situation	Emotion	Reactions

 After a week, review your entries. Write down any recurring themes, situations, or people that consistently trigger strong reactions in you. These patterns might indicate areas where your shadow is at work.

Repeating Unhealthy Patterns

Have you ever noticed that you keep making the same mistakes in your relationships or find yourself stuck in situations that seem to repeat like a broken record? These repetitive and often self-sabotaging patterns are often indicative of the influence of your shadow self.

Your shadow contains suppressed emotions, desires, and beliefs that you may not be consciously aware of. When these aspects of yourself remain unexamined and unacknowledged, they tend to manifest in your life as patterns that can be detrimental to your well-being.

Let's have a look at exactly how our shadow self can cause us to repeat unhealthy behavior patterns (Fosu, 2020):

◆ **Unconscious repression:** Your shadow self contains aspects of yourself that you have deemed unacceptable or have pushed away. These rejected parts can include unresolved traumas, fears, insecurities, and unmet needs. When these aspects are not integrated and addressed, they can drive you to repeat behaviors or make choices that lead to negative outcomes.

◆ **Seeking familiarity:** Human beings are creatures of habit, and we often seek out situations and relationships that feel familiar, even if they are unhealthy. Your shadow might be drawn to situations that replicate past experiences, whether they were positive or negative, as a way to maintain a sense of familiarity.

◆ **Projection onto others:** When your shadow remains unexplored, you may project these hidden aspects onto other people. For example, if you have unresolved anger within your shadow, you may consistently attract or clash with individuals who trigger that anger in you. This projection can perpetuate the cycle of unhealthy patterns.

 ### Exercise: Pattern Tracker

Think about recurring situations in your life where you've experienced negative outcomes or felt stuck. Write down these situations and the feelings associated with them.

Recurring Negative Situation	Feelings and Emotions

Now, identify the common threads among these situations. Jot down any similarities in how you react or the choices you make. These patterns may reveal your shadow's influence.

Reflections

Have you ever noticed that you sometimes have strong negative reactions or judgments toward certain people? These reactions can be powerful clues to the existence of your inner shadow. When you dislike or judge someone intensely, it often indicates that they are triggering something within you. This is known as projection. We touched on this above briefly. Projection occurs when you unconsciously attribute qualities, emotions, or behaviors that you don't want to acknowledge in yourself to someone else (Projection, 2022).

 ### *Mirror Exercise*

 Write down a list of people you strongly dislike or have conflicts with. Then, for each person, write down the qualities or behaviors that bother you about them.

Names	Qualities that Bother You

I would like you to take a moment to review this list. Write down any of these qualities that resonate with something you dislike or deny about yourself. This can be a powerful way to uncover hidden aspects of your shadow.

Dreams

Dreams are windows into the subconscious, and they often reveal our shadow selves. Dreams have long been regarded as a powerful tool for exploring the subconscious mind, and they play a crucial role in the process of shadow work. Your dreams are a canvas upon which your unconscious mind paints its stories, thoughts, emotions, and symbols. While your conscious mind is at rest, your unconscious self becomes more accessible, allowing hidden aspects of your psyche, including your shadow, to emerge.

Did you know that dreams often communicate in symbols and metaphors, making them a unique language of the unconscious? These symbols can represent repressed emotions, unresolved conflicts, and aspects of your shadow self that you may not be fully aware of in your waking life.

 ## *Exercise: Dream Journal*

 Keep this page open and by your bedside, along with a pen. Upon waking from a dream, immediately jot down everything you remember, including the storyline, characters, emotions, and any prominent symbols or events. Don't worry about making sense of it just yet; capture the raw details.

Dream 1:
_____
_____
_____
_____
_____

Dream 2:

_____

_____

_____

_____

_____

_____

Dream 3:

_____

_____

_____

_____

_____

_____

Dream 4:

_____

_____

_____

_____

_____

_____

Over time, review your dream journal and write down any recurring themes, symbols, or emotions. Pay special attention to dreams that evoke strong emotional reactions, whether positive or negative.

_____

_____

_____

_____

_____

Ask yourself if there are any aspects of your shadow self that seem to be emerging through your dreams. Write down any patterns or conflicts that parallel your waking experiences.

_____

_____

_____

_____

_____

_____

_____

_____

Fears and Reactions

Your fears and reactions are like signs on the road of self-discovery, pointing toward the hidden aspects of your shadow self. Your fears often conceal valuable information about your shadow self. These fears may be linked to experiences, traumas, or aspects of your personality that you've suppressed or denied. They can include fears of rejection, abandonment, failure, vulnerability, or even success.

 Exercise: Fear Exploration

Write down a list of your strongest fears or anxieties.

1. _____

_____

2. _____

_____

3. _____

_____

4. _____
_____

5. _____
_____

 For each fear, write down how you typically react when confronted by it.

Fear	Reaction

 Jot down whether you feel these reactions are appropriate or rooted in past experiences.

_____
_____
_____
_____
_____
_____
_____
_____
_____

By trying out these practical exercises, you'll gain valuable insights into your inner shadow. Remember to do them at your own pace and always take breaks when you feel overwhelmed.

Did you know that research tells us that confronting our shadow selves can offer us increased emotional intelligence, better mental health, and improved relationships (Guil et al., 2021)?

Maxine's Story

Meet Maxine, a woman who had been grappling with anxiety and emotional turmoil for as long as she could remember. At her workplace, she often found herself entangled in conflicts with her colleagues, and her stress levels were through the roof. She couldn't understand why she felt so out of control when it came to her emotions and her interactions with others.

One day, feeling at her wit's end, Maxine decided to give shadow work a try. She had heard about the power of it and was eager to explore her inner world to find answers to her struggles.

As Maxine looked more closely into her shadow work, she began to unravel the layers of her past. She realized that many of her triggers at work were connected to her childhood experiences of feeling powerless and unheard. Growing up, Maxine had often felt overshadowed by her siblings, leading her to believe that her voice didn't matter.

Through introspection and journaling, Maxine uncovered that she had been projecting her own deep-seated insecurities onto her colleagues. Her tendency to interpret innocent comments as personal attacks was a defense mechanism she had developed to protect herself from feeling powerless once more. She recognized that her emotional reactions were not solely about her coworkers but were rooted in her unresolved past.

Acknowledging her projections and the source of her emotional turmoil was a pivotal moment for Maxine. It wasn't an easy realization to confront, but it was the first step toward healing and personal growth. It was at this time that Maxine began to address her insecurities and childhood wounds.

She learned healthier coping mechanisms for dealing with her anxiety and triggers. Mindfulness and breathing exercises helped her stay grounded in the present moment, preventing her from spiraling into emotional chaos. Maxine also worked on developing better communication skills, allowing her to express herself without feeling threatened.

As Maxine continued her shadow work journey, a transformation took place within her. She started to notice significant improvements in her relationships at work. Instead of reacting defensively, she responded with empathy and understanding. Her colleagues began to perceive her as approachable and open, leading to more harmonious interactions.

Maxine's inner peace grew as she integrated the repressed aspects of her shadow. She no longer felt controlled by her emotions, and the weight of her childhood insecurities began to lift. Her newfound self-awareness allowed her to regulate her emotions more effectively, and she felt a sense of empowerment she had never experienced before.

Maxine's story serves as a powerful example of how shadow work can lead to self-awareness, personal growth, and emotional regulation. By acknowledging and addressing the hidden aspects of her shadow, she not only improved her relationships but also found inner peace and a deeper sense of self.

Unpacking Your Core and Shadow Beliefs

Let's look a little closer at core and shadow beliefs. These are the foundational beliefs that shape how you perceive yourself, others, and the world around you. Identifying and transmuting these beliefs is a powerful way to regain control over your emotions, heal, and experience positive transformation.

Here are some common core beliefs that do not help us:

♦ **I am not enough:** Many of us carry the belief that we are not worthy of love, success, or happiness. This belief can lead to feelings of inadequacy and self-doubt.

♦ **I am unlovable:** This belief can stem from past experiences of rejection or abandonment, leading to feelings of isolation and loneliness.

♦ **I must be perfect:** Striving for perfection can be paralyzing, causing anxiety and fear of failure.

♦ **I am a victim:** Believing that you are always at the mercy of external circumstances can disempower you and lead to resentment and anger.

♦ **I am responsible for everyone's happiness:** This belief can lead to people pleasing and neglecting your own needs, resulting in exhaustion and frustration.

We need to ask ourselves how we can change our perspective on these:

♦ **Self-awareness:** The first step is to become aware of your core beliefs. Pay attention to recurring thoughts and emotions. Journaling can be a helpful tool for this. Write down moments when you feel unworthy, unlovable, or overwhelmed.

◆ **Question your beliefs:** Challenge these beliefs. Ask yourself, "Is this belief based on facts or past experiences? Is it serving me well?" Often, you'll find that these beliefs are based on outdated information or other people's opinions.

◆ **Replace with empowering beliefs:** Once you've identified a disempowering belief, consciously choose to replace it with a more positive and empowering one. For example, replace "I am not enough" with "I am worthy of love and success just as I am."

◆ **Affirmations:** Create affirmations that support your new beliefs. Repeat them daily to reinforce the positive change. Affirmations can be a powerful tool for reprogramming your mind.

Cognitive Distortions

These are thought patterns that often lead to negative emotions and behaviors. They can be like a fog that clouds our judgment, making it challenging to see the truth about ourselves and the world around us. In shadow work, recognizing these distortions is crucial because they often connect to the hidden aspects of our psyche.

Here are some examples of cognitive distortions (Grinspoon, 2022):

◆ **Personalization:** Blaming oneself for events that are beyond their control. Example: "Our team lost because of me."

◆ **Catastrophizing:** Magnifying problems and imagining the worst-case scenarios. Example: "This spot on my skin is probably skin cancer; I'll be dead soon."

◆ **Fortune-telling:** Predicting negative outcomes without concrete evidence. Example: "My cholesterol is going to be sky-high."

- **Emotional reasoning:** Letting emotions dictate beliefs rather than relying on facts. Example: "I feel worthless, so I must be worthless."

- **Jumping to conclusions (mind-reading):** Assuming others' thoughts and intentions without evidence. Example: "The doctor is going to tell me I have cancer."

- **Black-and-white (all-or-nothing) thinking:** Seeing things as either perfect or a complete failure. Example: "I never have anything interesting to say."

- **Should-ing and must-ing:** Using self-critical language that imposes unnecessary pressure. Example: "I should be losing weight."

- **Overgeneralization:** Drawing broad, negative conclusions from a single event. Example: "I had one unhealthy meal; I'll always be unhealthy."

- **Comparison:** Measuring oneself against others without complete knowledge. Example: "All of my coworkers are happier than me."

- **Mental filter:** Focusing solely on negative aspects, ignoring positive elements. Example: "I am terrible at getting enough sleep."

- **Magnification and minimization:** Exaggerating negatives while downplaying positives. Example: "It was just one healthy meal."

- **Labeling:** Assigning negative labels to oneself based on past mistakes. Example: "I'm just not a healthy person."

- **Disqualifying the positive:** Dismissing positive achievements as luck or insignificant. Example: "I answered that well, but it was a lucky guess."

Exercise: Identifying Cognitive Distortions

 Take a moment to reflect on your thoughts and emotions throughout the day. When you find yourself experiencing a negative feeling, try to pinpoint the thought that triggered it. Ask yourself the following question:

What thought preceded this emotion? For example, if you're feeling anxious, the thought might be, "I'll never be good enough."

Negative Feeling	Thought Proceeding Negative Feeling

Write down which cognitive distortion this thought falls into. Use the list you've been provided above to identify the specific distortion(s). For instance, if the thought is all-or-nothing thinking (e.g., "I'll never be good enough"), write that down.

Thought	Cognitive Distortion

Being mindful of cognitive distortions is a huge step toward uncovering your shadow beliefs and experiencing personal growth. Take your time, be gentle with yourself, and remember that it's normal to encounter these distortions–what matters is how you address them.

Analyzing Your Triggers

Triggers are situations, events, or even words that bring up strong and often uncomfortable emotions within us. They can make us feel out of control, and it's crucial to recognize them so you can work through them effectively.

You might be wondering how you can identify a trigger. You should start by paying close attention to your emotional reactions. Here's how:

◆ **Notice unusual emotional intensity:** If you find yourself feeling extremely angry, anxious, sad, or any intense emotion that seems out of proportion to the situation, that's a clue.

◆ **Take a step back:** When you notice such intense emotions, pause for a moment. Ask yourself if what just happened warrants this level of reaction. Is the situation really as bad as it seems at that moment?

Remember, triggers are your subconscious mind's way of alerting you to unresolved issues. Here's what you can do next:

◆ **Pause and breathe:** When you notice a trigger, the first step is to pause. Take a deep breath. This simple act can help you regain control over your emotions.

◆ **Self-compassion:** Be gentle with yourself. It's okay to feel what you feel. Your emotions are valid, even if they seem disproportionate. Try saying to yourself, "It's okay, I'm just triggered right now, and that's okay."

◆ **Ask, "Why?":** Reflect on why this situation triggered such a strong reaction. Dig deep into your past experiences and beliefs. Often, triggers are connected to unresolved issues from your past.

Studies have shown that recognizing and working through triggers is a vital part of emotional regulation and personal growth. By addressing these triggers, individuals can experience reduced anxiety, improved emotional stability, and enhanced overall well-being (Veazey, 2022). So, rest assured, you're on the right path.

Interactive Element

 Exercise: Examine Your Inner "Tapes"

> Take some time to think about the negative comments or criticisms that others have made about you. It could be something a parent, friend, or even a colleague said. Write them down.

_____

_____

_____

_____

_____

_____

_____

_____

> Reflect on the beliefs you hold about yourself that are negative or self-critical. Write them down.

_____

_____

_____

_____

_____

Recall moments in your life when these negative beliefs about yourself did not hold true. List examples of when you proved these beliefs wrong.

Identify evidence that contradicts these negative beliefs. What strengths, achievements, or qualities do you possess that show you are not defined by these beliefs?

Exercise: Unpack Your Triggers

Recall a recent situation where you felt an intense emotional reaction. Write down the triggering event in detail.

_____
_____
_____
_____
_____
_____
_____
_____

Consider not only the physical manifestation (e.g., yelling, crying) but, more importantly, the feelings driving that physical manifestation. Write down your emotional response.

_____
_____
_____
_____
_____

Write down why you think you reacted the way you did. Were there underlying emotions or past experiences that contributed to your reaction?

_____
_____
_____
_____
_____

Core Beliefs Journal Prompts

Use these prompts to journal and explore your core beliefs.

If I could change anything about myself it would be...

I feel most vulnerable when...

I learned this belief from...

I can challenge this belief by...

_____
_____
_____
_____
_____
_____
_____

I believe I am worthy of love and acceptance because...

_____
_____
_____
_____
_____
_____
_____

In this chapter, I've laid the foundation for your journey by providing practical and easy-to-understand steps for self-reflection and understanding your triggers. You've begun to shine a light on those hidden corners of your psyche, where your shadow self resides.

Shadow work is a gentle, compassionate journey of self-discovery and healing. You've already shown great courage by embarking on this adventure, and for that, you should be proud.

In the chapters to come, we'll dive even deeper, customizing a toolbox of specialized techniques for shadow work. These techniques will help you navigate the complexities of your inner world and guide you toward greater self-awareness, emotional regulation, and personal growth.

So, take a moment to acknowledge your bravery, your desire for self-healing, and your commitment to growth. The road ahead may have its challenges, but it's also filled with incredible rewards.

Turn the page, and let's delve deeper into your shadow work toolbox. The adventure continues!

Illuminate The Path For Those Who Walk Behind You on This Journey of Self-Discovery

In the labyrinth of self-discovery, where the corridors of our subconscious hide the keys to our most profound insights, a powerful tool lies: self-guided shadow work. For those who have embarked on this introspective journey, you know the transformative power these pages hold. They are not mere collections of paper but vessels of self-revelation, guiding us through the murky waters of our inner world.

Now, imagine standing at the edge of a vast ocean, the waves whispering secrets of ancient wisdom. This ocean is the collective consciousness of all who seek understanding, healing, and growth through shadow work. This workbook and journal are not just your boat in this vastness but also your map and compass. The insights you've gleaned, the revelations unearthed, and the transformations undergone are treasures you've discovered along the way.

However, a treasure shared is a treasure multiplied. Leaving a review for this workbook and journal casts a stone into this vast ocean, creating ripples that extend far beyond your sight. Each ripple reaches others navigating their own introspective journeys, guiding them, encouraging them, and letting them know they are not alone in these uncharted waters.

Your review serves as a lighthouse for fellow travelers lost in the fog of their subconscious. It offers hope and reassurance that their path, though challenging, is traversable and transformative. Your words can illuminate the benefits of shadow work, shedding light on how it has changed your perspective, relationships, and life.

Sharing your challenges and triumphs can inspire others to take the first step, pick up this workbook, and confront their shadows with hope and determination.

Thank you for your bravery, your vulnerability, and your support. Your voice matters, and your experience is a gift to those who seek to follow in your footsteps. Together, we can help others find the courage to face their shadows and emerge into the light of profound self-awareness and healing.

Scan the QR code to leave a quick review.

CHAPTER 5
THE TOOLBOX-
SPECIALIZED
TECHNIQUES FOR
SHADOW WORK

The Toolbox-Specialized Techniques for Shadow Work

> *Unless you learn to face your own shadows, you will continue to see them in others, because the world outside of you is only a reflection of the world inside of you. –The Minds Journal*

We're taking another step forward, and I'm excited to share a toolbox filled with more shadow work techniques. These techniques can be added to the ones explored in the previous chapter to build the strategies you need to continue.

In this chapter, I've included the techniques with you in mind. They are simple, budget-friendly, and tailored to beginners like yourself. As usual, the goal is to create a safe and inviting space where you can explore your shadow self at your own pace without feeling overwhelmed.

Each one is a tool that can help you uncover hidden aspects of yourself, understand your emotions, and, ultimately, transform your life for the better.

Let's begin.

The Dialogue Exercise: Talking to Your Shadow

Find a quiet and comfortable space where you won't be disturbed. Sit or lie down in a relaxed position, and take a few deep breaths to center yourself.

Close your eyes and imagine yourself in front of a group of hypercritical people, or even just one person, who tends to trigger feelings of insecurity and self-consciousness within you. It could be someone from your past or present.

> **Now, see yourself through their eyes. Write down what you think you look like to them. This version of yourself, the one you see from their perspective, is your shadow. It might look very different from the person you typically think of as "you."**

Focus on this version of yourself, your Shadow, without judgment. Acknowledge its presence and understand that it's a part of you, just like any other aspect.

In your mind, reach out and form an unbreakable bond with your Shadow. Imagine a strong connection between you and it. Feel this connection physically, as if you are holding hands, hugging, or simply being close to it.

Speak to your Shadow with kindness and assurance. Say, "You're with me at all times." As you say these words, imagine the bond growing stronger, and feel the connection becoming more tangible.

Recognize that by forming this bond, you are taking the first step toward a powerful tool known as "Inner Authority." It's an authority that emanates from within yourself, allowing you and your Shadow to speak with one unified voice.

Embrace this newfound authority. It's different from what you're accustomed to because it arises from deep within you, integrating all aspects of your being.

With your Inner Authority, you can begin to explore and heal in ways you might not have thought possible. Your shadow is no longer something to be feared or ignored but a valuable part of your journey towards self-discovery and growth.

Take a moment to sit in this newfound awareness, appreciating the connection you've formed with your Shadow and the Inner Authority that is now at your disposal.

The Visualization Exercise: A Mental Journey

This meditation is designed to create a safe and introspective space where you can explore and integrate your shadow aspects.

 Begin by setting a clear intention for your meditation. Write down what you hope to gain from this experience and what you are ready to release. Is there a specific emotion, fear, or negative behavior you'd like to explore and understand better? Take a moment to clarify your intentions.

_____

_____

_____

_____

_____

_____

_____

_____

_____

Find a calm, quiet spot where you won't be bothered. It could be in your cozy room or a peaceful outdoor area where you feel relaxed.

- Choose a position you feel comfortable and safe in. Take some slow, deep breaths to relax your body and let go of any tension in your muscles. Try to block out any distractions and focus your attention inside yourself.

- Concentrate on your breathing. As you breathe in and out, let your breath be like an anchor that calms your thoughts. You should expect your mind to wander this is normal. Gently take a breath and bring it back to the present.

- Start imagining your shadow self. Picture any hidden emotions, fears, or negative habits that you usually keep buried. Don't judge or push them away just let them come into your mind.

- Accept your shadow self with an open heart. Realize that these parts of you are just as natural as any other and not necessarily good or bad. Let go of any preconceived ideas and simply acknowledge that they are a part of you.

◆ Now, I want you to visualize yourself physically letting go of the emotional baggage you've been holding onto. Picture your fears, insecurities, and negative habits as heavy burdens. With each breath out, imagine these burdens getting lighter, leaving you feeling freer.

◆ Slowly merge your shadow self with your conscious awareness. Understand that by doing this, you're becoming more complete and genuine. Imagine your light and shadow aspects coming together, creating a balanced and harmonious inner self.

 As you finish this visualization, take a moment to write down any new thoughts or feelings that came up during the process. Remember, shadow work is an ongoing journey; each time you explore it, you'll discover more about yourself and grow.

A Role-Playing Exercise: Embodying Your Shadow

Find a quiet and comfortable space where you won't be disturbed. Take a few deep breaths to relax and center yourself.

 Write down aspects of yourself or emotions that you may have been suppressing, denying, or avoiding. These are often elements of your shadow self.

1. _____

_____

2. _____

_____

3. _____

_____

4. _____

_____

5. _____

_____

6. _____

_____

 Now, write down one specific aspect or emotion you want to explore during this exercise. It could be anger, jealousy, fear, insecurity, or any other emotion or trait.

_____

_____

Write down a name and a persona to the aspect of your shadow self you've chosen. Imagine this character as a separate entity, distinct from your usual self.

Character Name:

_____

Character Persona:

_____
_____
_____
_____
_____
_____
_____

Write down a description of the character's appearance, personality, and behaviors. How does this persona express the chosen shadow aspect?

Character's Appearance:

_____
_____
_____
_____
_____
_____

Character's Personality:

_____
_____
_____
_____
_____
_____

Character's Behaviors:

_____

_____

_____

_____

_____

_____

Character's Emotions:

_____

_____

_____

_____

_____

_____

Begin to embody your created persona. Act out or role-play as this character. Imagine how they would react in different situations. Pay attention to how it feels to express the chosen shadow aspect through this character. Write down any physical sensations, emotions, or thoughts that arise.

Physical Sensations:

_____

_____

Emotions:

_____

_____

Thoughts:

_____

_____

After a few minutes of role-playing, pause and return to your normal self. Write down your experiences and observations. Answer questions like:

What did it feel like to express this shadow aspect through the persona?

_____

_____

_____

_____

_____

_____

_____

Were there any surprising insights or emotions that emerged during the role-playing?

_____

_____

_____

_____

_____

_____

_____

How did your body react to this exploration?

_____
_____
_____
_____
_____
_____
_____

Did you notice any resistance or discomfort?

_____
_____
_____
_____
_____
_____
_____

What did you learn about this aspect of your shadow self?

_____
_____
_____
_____
_____
_____
_____

Reflect on how you can integrate the insights gained from this exercise into your daily life. Consider whether there are healthy ways to express and address this shadow aspect.

You can repeat this exercise with different aspects of your shadow self over time to gain a deeper understanding of your inner dynamics.

The Affirmation Exercise: Reinforcing Positive Change

Reflect on the affirmations, one by one. Take a few deep breaths and repeat the affirmation to yourself several times. Allow each affirmation to sink in and resonate with you.

 After repeating the affirmation, write your thoughts and feelings about it. Explore any emotions that come up and consider how the affirmation relates to your life, experiences, and inner self.

Affirmations	Thoughts & Feelings Evoked
1. I choose to face my issues.	
2. I am not to blame for my trauma.	
3. I deserve respect.	
4. I will live in the present.	
5. I am going to grow and learn from pain.	
6. I am in love with who I am.	
7. I forgive myself for my shadow side.	
8. I am grateful.	
9. I acknowledge and accept my true self.	
10. My mistakes do not define me.	
11. My past is not my future.	
12. I am worthy of love.	
13. I am learning who I am as a whole.	
14. I can decide my future.	

15. I want to move forward.	
16. I want to heal.	
17. I will no longer hold grudges.	
18. I own my mistakes.	
19. I only need validation from me.	
20. Those who are mean do not deserve my energy.	
21. I deserve boundaries.	
22. Owning my emotions makes me stronger.	
23. The person I'm becoming is amazing.	
24. I choose to learn from my mistakes.	

For each affirmation, think about how you can incorporate it into your daily life and shadow work journey. What actions or mindset shifts can you make to align with the affirmation?

Continue this process with each selected affirmation, taking your time to truly internalize and work with each one.

Finally, consider how these affirmations collectively contribute to your shadow work and personal development. Write down the progress you've made and the areas where you still have room for growth.

Repeat this exercise regularly to deepen your shadow work and self-awareness. Over time, you may find that these affirmations help you uncover and heal hidden aspects of yourself while empowering you to move forward with a more positive and self-compassionate mindset.

The Self-Compassion Exercise: Embracing Your Shadow with Love

Sit or lie down in a comfortable position. You can also do this exercise while standing or walking if that feels more natural to you.

To start, take a few deep cleansing breaths. In through your nose and out through your mouth. Continue to breathe deeply and slowly, paying full attention to your breath.

Close your eyes and bring to mind an aspect of yourself or a past event you have been avoiding or denying, representing your shadow self. It could be a negative belief, a past mistake, or a quality you're not proud of.

While focusing on this aspect of your shadow, repeat self-compassionate phrases silently in your mind, such as:

- ✓ "I acknowledge and accept this part of myself."

- ✓ "I am human, and I make mistakes."

- ✓ "It's okay to have flaws and imperfections."

- ✓ "I am worthy of love and acceptance, even with this shadow."

As you continue to breathe and repeat these phrases, visualize a warm and loving light surrounding the aspect of yourself or the event that represents your shadow. Imagine this light enveloping it with acceptance and understanding.

As you continue to breathe and visualize, imagine that this aspect of your shadow is starting to soften and dissolve. Feel any tension or resistance in your body slowly releasing.

Offer yourself kindness and forgiveness for carrying this shadow. Remind yourself that you are not defined by your shadow, and it is a part of your humanity.

With your eyes still closed, place your hand on your heart as a physical gesture of self-compassion. Feel the warmth and connection to your own heart.

Conclude the meditation by expressing gratitude to yourself for engaging in this self-compassion exercise and for your willingness to work with your shadow.

When you're ready, slowly open your eyes and return to the present moment.

This self-compassion meditation can help you integrate and make peace with your shadow self. It allows you to connect with your inner self and provide the love and acceptance that every part of you deserves. Feel free to write down any emotions you felt during your meditation.

The Art Therapy Exercise: Expressing Your Shadow Creatively

Before beginning this exercise, you will want to gather the following materials:

- Blank canvas or paper
- Various art supplies—colored pencils, markers, acrylic paints, charcoal, pastels.
- Brushes if you're using paint.
- Water and a container for your brushes.
- An open and curious mindset.

Create a calm and inviting environment for your art therapy session. Play soothing music, light a candle, or do whatever helps you get into a creative and introspective mood.

 Take a few moments to reflect on the aspects of yourself or past experiences that you consider to be part of your shadow self. These could be qualities, emotions, or memories that you've suppressed, denied, or are reluctant to acknowledge. Take a moment to write them down.

◆ Select an art medium that resonates with you and feels comfortable. You can choose to work with colors, paint, charcoal, or any other medium that allows you to express yourself.

◆ Begin by creating a self-portrait on your canvas or paper. It doesn't need to be highly detailed or realistic; the focus here is on self-expression. Capture your facial expression, posture, and any emotions you associate with your shadow self.

◆ Use colors, shapes, and symbols to represent the aspects of your shadow self within the self-portrait. For example, if you're exploring feelings of anger or sadness, you might use red or blue hues to convey those emotions. If you're exploring a particular quality, like perfectionism, you could incorporate patterns or symbols that represent that trait.

◆ Allow yourself to express your feelings and thoughts through your art freely. Don't worry about making it look "good" or "perfect." This is about honest expression.

◆ As you work on your self-portrait, engage in an internal dialogue with the aspects of your shadow self. Ask questions like, "Why are you here?" "What do you need?" "How can I integrate or understand you better?" Write down any insights or responses that come up during this process.

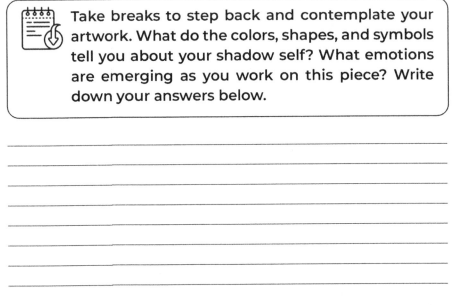

Take breaks to step back and contemplate your artwork. What do the colors, shapes, and symbols tell you about your shadow self? What emotions are emerging as you work on this piece? Write down your answers below.

_____

_____

_____

_____

_____

_____

_____

_____

Once your self-portrait feels complete, sit with it for a while. Reflect on what you've created and the insights you've gained through the process.

Remember that art therapy is a deeply personal and therapeutic process. There are no right or wrong ways to create your self-portrait, and it's more about the process of self-discovery and expression than the final result. Be gentle with yourself and use this exercise as an opportunity to explore and understand your shadow self in a creative and healing way.

Interactive Element: Deep Shadow Work Journal Prompts

Journaling is a valuable tool in the world of shadow work. If you struggle with what to write, you should know this is normal, and it happens to all of us. I wanted to include a lot of journal prompts to help you with that.

What values were instilled in you during your upbringing?

_____

_____

_____

_____

Identify the triggers that cause physical tension in your body.

_____

_____

_____

_____

How would your friends and family describe your personality?

_____

_____

_____

_____

What aspects of yourself do you wish your friends and family were aware of?

_____

_____

_____

_____

Share something you find challenging to confess to others.

_____
_____
_____
_____

What skills or abilities do you wish you could improve upon?

_____
_____
_____
_____

Reflect on the three most significant relationships in your life and how they have shaped your self-perception.

_____
_____
_____
_____

What types of individuals are drawn to you as friends or acquaintances?

_____
_____
_____
_____

Anonymously share a personal secret with the world if given the chance.

_____
_____
_____
_____

Describe the time and circumstances when you last experienced genuine inner peace.

_____
_____
_____
_____

What aspects of yourself make you feel inferior to others, and how do colleagues at work perceive you?

_____
_____
_____
_____

What misconceptions do people commonly hold about you in your professional life?

_____
_____
_____
_____

What do you wish people at work understood better about you?

_____
_____
_____
_____

If you could start your career anew, what choices or actions would you change?

_____
_____
_____
_____

What work-related responsibilities drain your energy the most?

_____

_____

_____

_____

Explore the work requests that evoke negative reactions within you and examine the reasons behind them.

_____

_____

_____

_____

What changes would you make in your workplace or career if you could?

_____

_____

_____

_____

Do you desire a different manner of treatment from your colleagues at work? If so, how?

_____

_____

_____

_____

Identify the expectations at work that feel challenging to meet.

_____

_____

_____

_____

As we conclude this chapter, you've taken the necessary steps in constructing your personal toolbox for shadow work—a collection of introspective and self-awareness tools that will serve as your companions on this transformative journey. You've delved into various prompts and techniques, gaining insights into your hidden aspects, inner conflicts, and unresolved emotions. Remember, shadow work is an ongoing process, and your toolbox will continue to evolve and grow.

In the next chapter, we will explore even more powerful and practical strategies to deepen your understanding of yourself, confront buried traumas, and navigate the complexities of your inner world. These advanced but still easy-to-understand tools will equip you with the means to unravel deeper layers of your psyche, fostering growth, healing, and self-acceptance. Prepare to explore the uncharted territories of your consciousness, armed with a wealth of knowledge and newfound resilience.

CHAPTER 6
FURTHER INTO THE SHADOWS

Further Into the Shadows

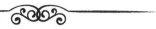

>
>
> *What you are, you do not see. What you see is your shadow. –Rabindranath Tagore*

In the previous chapters, we've laid the foundation, explored the basics, and even started working with some practical skills to help you navigate the uncharted territories of your inner world. You are doing an incredible job!

Now, it's time to take a slightly deeper plunge into the waters of shadow work. But don't worry we won't be diving into anything too overwhelming or intimidating. This chapter is designed to gently introduce you to more advanced shadow work concepts and techniques without pushing you too far.

If you're feeling a bit apprehensive about this next step, that's perfectly normal. Remember, shadow work is a journey, and taking it at your own pace is entirely okay. We're here to support you every step of the way, providing guidance, compassion, and understanding.

As we venture into more advanced concepts, remember that this is all in service of your personal growth and self-healing. The goal isn't perfection; it's progress. So, take a deep breath, trust the process, and know you're in good hands.

In the following pages, I'll offer you techniques that will empower you to navigate the complexities of your inner world with greater ease and understanding. You'll uncover ways to heal old wounds, release what no longer serves you, and further integrate the various facets of your whole self.

I believe in your capacity for growth and healing.

Unveiling Your Childhood

Let's begin by shining a light on your childhood and those wounds that might still be affecting you today. We all carry baggage from our past, and recognizing these wounds is the first step in healing. Here are some common examples (Sansone et al., 2012):

◆ **Abandonment:** This wound can stem from a caregiver's absence or inconsistency in your early years. It might manifest as an intense fear of rejection or a tendency to cling to relationships for fear of being left alone.

◆ **Neglect:** Childhood neglect, whether emotional or physical, can lead to feelings of unworthiness or self-doubt. You might find it hard to prioritize your needs or have a constant inner critic.

◆ **Trauma:** Traumatic experiences during childhood can leave deep scars. These could include physical, emotional, or sexual abuse. The signs may be vivid nightmares, flashbacks, or severe anxiety.

◆ **Criticism:** Constant criticism from parents or authority figures can lead to low self-esteem and a harsh inner critic. You might struggle with perfectionism and a constant need for external validation.

◆ **Loss:** Losing a loved one at a young age can create issues around grief and loss that linger into adulthood. It might manifest as difficulties in forming and maintaining relationships.

Knowing how to recognize that your inner child is wounded is key. If you want to explore inner child healing and any hurts or traumas from childhood, I would like to recommend the last book I published, Reparent Your Wounded Inner Child. It is a gentle, helpful tool to take on that journey with you. Now, let's review some signs that may resonate with your inner wounded child:

- **Emotional overreactions:** You find yourself reacting strongly to situations that may seem minor to others.

- **Repetition of patterns:** You notice that you keep repeating the same destructive patterns in relationships or life choices.

- **Self-sabotage:** You engage in self-destructive behaviors, perhaps unconsciously, like procrastination, substance abuse, or self-harm.

- **Low self-esteem:** You struggle with self-worth, often feeling like you're not good enough.

- **Avoidance:** You avoid confronting your past, either by numbing your emotions or diverting your attention.

Our childhood experiences shape our beliefs and behaviors. During your formative years, you learned how to navigate the world around you, but sometimes, you picked up limiting beliefs and coping mechanisms that no longer serve you.

For instance, if you grew up in an environment where emotions were repressed, you might have learned to suppress your own feelings. If you faced constant criticism, you might have developed perfectionistic tendencies. These learned behaviors and beliefs can influence your adult life in ways you might not even be aware of.

Jesse's Story

Growing up with a mentally ill mother impacted me far beyond my ability to comprehend until recently. I carried my work stress home. If I was working on a project, any project, it had to be perfect, even if that meant staying late or working on it at home well into the night. I never looked into a mirror and felt confident. I would starve myself, even as an adult, if I got dressed in the morning and anything felt tight. My appearance needed to be perfect, or I wouldn't be accepted. In any relationship I had, I would spiral at the slightest comment. It could be something as simple as "Hey, could we meet an hour later tomorrow? Something has come up." I would hear: *They want to limit how much time we spend together because I am so annoying.*

You see, I grew up with a father who criticized everything I ever did. I was never smart enough. I was never funny enough. I was never fit enough. As an adult, this formed my need for perfectionism. This was my coping mechanism. What I found out through shadow work was I never believed any of these things about myself. In fact, I found myself to be pretty awesome. These were the beliefs of my father, not me. I was able to relax, let go of needing to be perfect all the time, and uncover my true self.

Healing Exercises

Now, let's talk about the good stuff—healing. Remember, this is a process, and it's okay to take it one step at a time. Here are some practical strategies to help you begin your healing journey:

 Start by offering yourself the same compassion you'd give to anyone you love. Jot down five things you truly admire about yourself.

1. _____
_____

2. _____
_____

3. _____
_____

4. _____
_____

5. _____
_____

Write down your thoughts, feelings, and memories of your childhood. What do you think you may still be holding on to? This can help you gain insight into your past and how it's affecting your present.

_____
_____
_____
_____
_____
_____

Consider talking to someone you trust, like a good friend. They can provide guidance and a safe space for exploring your childhood wounds and have a perspective you may not be able to see just yet. Write down anything you learned from your conversation.

_____
_____
_____
_____

Visualize and connect with your inner child. Write down five things you want to say to them. Remind them you are there to love and support them now. This can be a powerful way to heal past wounds.

1. _____

2. _____

3. _____

4. _____

5. _____

 Learning to set healthy boundaries is vital for protecting yourself from repeating old patterns of hurt. Write down three boundaries you want to put in place and one you are going to put in place immediately.

1. _____

2. _____

3. _____

◆ **Circle the boundary you will put in place immediatly.**

This is the time to be gentle with yourself and celebrate every small step forward. Studies have shown that childhood wounds can have a significant impact on our mental and emotional well-being throughout our lives. Research indicates that addressing these wounds through self-reflection can lead to improved mental health, healthier relationships, and increased overall life satisfaction (Sansone et al., 2012).

Using Your Guilt as a Tool

Let's start by demystifying guilt. Guilt is that uncomfortable feeling we experience when we believe we've done something wrong or failed to meet our own or society's standards. It's a common emotion that can be triggered by various situations or actions. While it may initially seem like a burden, guilt serves a valuable purpose in our lives.

Think of guilt as a mirror reflecting your values and moral compass. It's your conscience nudging you to pay attention to something important. When you feel guilty, it's often a sign that there's something within you that needs your attention and understanding.

Guilt can be closely tied to your shadow self. Your shadow self is the part of you that contains unacknowledged or suppressed emotions, desires, and experiences. Guilt can often be a manifestation of these hidden aspects, trying to get your attention.

Embracing guilt means embracing an opportunity for growth. When you confront your guilt head-on, you're taking a brave step toward understanding yourself better. It's a chance to bring those shadowy aspects into the light and work through them.

Managing Unhelpful Guilt Exercises

Now that you understand the purpose of guilt let's explore some exercises to manage it effectively. Remember, our goal is not to eliminate guilt but to harness its power for your personal development.

 ### *Self-Compassion*

Begin by showing yourself kindness and understanding. Understand that it's okay to feel guilty sometimes; it's a part of being human. Treat yourself as you would a close friend, with love and empathy.

> Write down a recent guilt-inducing situation. Then, list three ways to offer yourself self-compassion in response to this guilt.

1. _____
_____
2. _____
_____
3. _____
_____

 ### *Identify the Root Cause*

Explore the underlying cause of your guilt. Ask yourself why you feel this way and what values or beliefs are being challenged. This can help you unearth hidden aspects of your shadow self.

> Take a moment to dig deeper into a specific guilt-triggering event from your past. What values or beliefs were challenged? What can you learn from this situation?

_____
_____
_____
_____
_____

 ## *Forgiveness*

Forgiveness doesn't always mean forgiving others; it can also mean forgiving yourself. Accept that you're not perfect, and you will make mistakes. Forgiving yourself is a crucial step in healing and growth.

 Reflect on a situation where you need to forgive yourself. Write a forgiveness letter to yourself, acknowledging your imperfections and granting yourself the gift of forgiveness.

I forgive myself for:

_____
_____
_____
_____
_____
_____
_____

 ## *Seek Support*

Don't hesitate to seek support from friends, family, or anyone you trust. Talking about your guilt with someone you trust can provide valuable insights and emotional relief.

Reach out to a trusted friend or family member and have an open conversation about a recent guilt-triggering event. Share your feelings. Write down what you took away from their perspective.

 Take Action

Guilt often arises from a sense of powerlessness. To transform guilt into growth, take constructive actions that align with your values and help you make amends, if necessary.

 Write down one small action you can take to address the source of your guilt. It could be an apology, a commitment to change, or a kind gesture toward someone.

Several studies suggest that acknowledging and working through guilt can lead to improved emotional well-being and reduced symptoms of anxiety and depression (Keng et al., 2011). These findings highlight the potential benefits of embracing your guilt.

As you explore your own shadow work, it's essential to remember that guilt, though intimidating at times, serves as a valuable tool for self-discovery and personal growth. You can harness this emotion to facilitate your transformation, leading you toward healing and enhanced self-regulation.

Healing Shame

Shame is that feeling deep within us that tells us we are fundamentally flawed, unworthy, or unlovable. It often stems from early life experiences, societal expectations, and even cultural norms. It's essential to understand that shame is a natural human emotion, and everyone experiences it to some degree. However, it becomes problematic when it festers in the shadows of our psyche, affecting our self-esteem, relationships, and overall well-being.

Why shame is not helpful:

- **It's paralyzing:** Shame can keep us stuck in a cycle of self-criticism and self-doubt, preventing personal growth.

- **It's isolating:** When we feel ashamed, we tend to hide our true selves, disconnecting from others and hindering genuine connections.

- **It hinders self-acceptance:** True self-acceptance requires acknowledging our shadows and working through shame to embrace all aspects of ourselves.

Exercises

 Write down instances when you've felt shame and explore the underlying beliefs and triggers. Challenge these negative thoughts with self-affirmations.

_____

_____

_____

 Write down five affirmations that can reinforce your self-worth and self-acceptance. Repeat them daily to reprogram your subconscious mind.

1. _____
   _____
2. _____
   _____
3. _____
   _____
4. _____
   _____
5. _____
   _____

Remember, healing shame is a process, and it's okay to take small steps. You are brave for embarking on this journey. Each day, you'll move closer to the peace and healing you deserve.

Examine the Ego

Our ego is like a protective shield that we all have. It's the part of us that forms our identity, helps us navigate the world, and keeps us safe from harm. It's essential for our survival, but sometimes it can become too dominant, leading to a range of negative emotions and behaviors.

 Exercise: Ego Awareness

 Take a few moments once a day for a week to reflect on moments when you felt strong emotions. Write down the situations and try to identify which emotions were triggered by your ego. This will help you become more aware of its influence on your life.

	Situation that triggered a strong emotional reaction	Emotions Triggered
Monday		
Tuesday		
Wednesday		
Thursday		
Friday		
Saturday		
Sunday		

Mastering your ego doesn't mean eliminating it but rather understanding and balancing it. Here are some practical tips to help you on this journey:

◆ **Self-reflection:** Set aside time each day for introspection. Continue to journal your thoughts and feelings to gain insights into your ego's patterns.

◆ **Mindfulness meditation:** Practice mindfulness to observe your thoughts without judgment. This can help you detach from your ego's narratives.

◆ **Seek feedback:** Ask those closest to you for honest feedback about your ego-driven behaviors. This external perspective can be eye-opening.

◆ **Cultivate humility:** Recognize that you're not perfect and your ego has flaws. Embrace your imperfections as opportunities for growth.

◆ **Engage in self-compassion:** You need to start treating yourself exactly as you treat those you love.

Ego-Balancing Journal

> Write down instances when you noticed your ego at play, and reflect on how you can balance it with humility and self-compassion.

_____

_____

_____

_____

_____

_____

Being a Mirror to Ourselves

It is believed that the best way to understand your shadow is by analyzing your most difficult relationships. Let's explore how the people around us can reflect our innermost struggles and offer valuable insights into our shadow selves.

> Begin by making a list of the people with whom you've had challenging or emotionally charged interactions. These could be family members, friends, coworkers, or even acquaintances.
>
> For each person on your list, jot down the emotions or reactions they provoke in you. Are they making you feel angry, anxious, or insecure? What are the recurring patterns or themes in these relationships?

Names	Emotions they provoke in you

 Explore your triggers by asking yourself why these interactions affect you so deeply. What is it about their behavior or words that hit a nerve? Are there any past experiences or wounds that may be contributing to your reactions?

_____

_____

_____

_____

Recognize that these challenging relationships are mirrors reflecting your own unresolved issues or unacknowledged emotions. As you dig deeper, you'll uncover aspects of your shadow self that you may not have been aware of before.

Approach this process with self-compassion. Remember that shadow work is about healing and growth, not self-blame. Embrace your shadows as a part of your whole self.

Interactive Element

Family Tree Exercise

Examine your family tree

Make a family tree of your two sets of grandparents, all of your aunts and uncles, and your parents because they're the generations above you whose attributes—good and bad—might be in you.

The Generations Above You

Mom's Family Tree

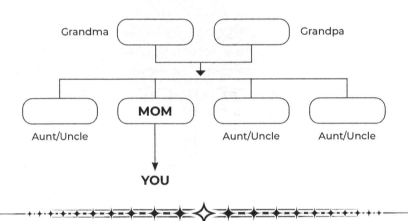

Dad's Family Tree

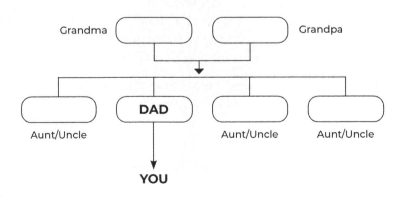

Now, you need to take a good look at all the qualities that you notice within your family and ask yourself which of those you notice within you.

Look for family behavioral patterns and write down what you uncover.

Family Member's Name	Qualities They Have That You Notice Within You

 ## *Exercise: Talk to Your Inner Child*

Find a childhood photo that resonates with you.

 Talk to them and ask them what they need now or what they needed back then.

Write down what you think those answers would be.

_____

Exercise: People as Mirrors

Think of someone who bothers you, and reflect on what it is about that person that might also be within you.

What is it about this person that I don't like?

_____
_____
_____
_____
_____

Do I find that I have some of those same traits sometimes?

_____
_____
_____
_____
_____
_____
_____

What makes it so difficult to be around them?

When that person is around me, what parts of me do I notice brighten up?

And how do I feel about that part of myself?'

In this chapter, we've delved into more advanced concepts of shadow work, exploring the intricacies of our hidden aspects with depth and courage. You've journeyed through the labyrinth of your psyche, uncovering layers of your shadow self that may have been concealed for years. As you continue on this path of self-discovery, it's important to acknowledge the progress you've made and the insights you've gained.

Now, as we move forward into the next chapter, we'll explore the vital process of integrating your shadow self. This is where you can expect real transformation to happen. Integrating your shadow isn't about erasing or denying these aspects but embracing them as a part of your whole self. It's about harnessing the wisdom and strength that lies within your shadow and using it to propel your personal growth.

So, as you turn the page and embark on the next stage of your journey, be prepared to merge your newfound awareness with your conscious self. By integrating your shadow, you'll find a sense of wholeness and authenticity that can lead to a more fulfilling and empowered life. Embrace this next chapter with an open heart and an open mind, for it holds the key to unlocking your true potential.

CHAPTER 7
INTEGRATING YOUR
SHADOW SELF

Integrating Your Shadow Self

> *If you don't accept yourself, you can't transcend yourself and the world: first, you need to increase your awareness, then you need to accept what you learn, then you need to take action.* **–Oli Anderson**

Your shadow self is not broken. It's not a problem to be fixed but rather a facet of your complete self waiting to be acknowledged and integrated. Just like every part of you, your shadow self has its own stories, experiences, and wisdom to offer.

In this chapter, we'll explore the idea that some aspects of your shadow self are not inherently negative or destructive. Instead, they are there to teach you something valuable about yourself. By understanding and integrating these aspects, you can become a more whole and authentic version of yourself.

Think of your shadow self as a puzzle piece that's been hidden away for far too long. As we gently uncover and fit these pieces into the mosaic of your self-awareness, you'll find that the picture of who you truly are becomes clearer and more beautiful than ever before.

So, let's start this journey together with an open heart and a willingness to embrace all that makes you, you. We'll explore practical exercises, thoughtful reflections, and supportive guidance to help you integrate your shadow self in a safe and inviting space.

By the end of this chapter, you'll see that your shadow self isn't something to be feared but something to be welcomed as an integral part of your journey toward personal growth and self-acceptance.

What Is Shadow Self-Integration

At its core, shadow integration is about bringing the hidden parts of yourself into the light of your awareness. Imagine these hidden parts as the shadows that exist just beyond the reach of a flashlight. These shadows, often referred to as your "shadow self," contain both positive and negative aspects of your personality, and they're elements that you've pushed away or denied for various reasons.

Think of it this way: Imagine a coin with two sides. One side represents the traits that society, your family, or your peers have labeled as "bad" or "immoral." These might include things like anger, sexuality, or untamed impulses. These traits were likely suppressed because they didn't align with the values of the people around you.

Now, flip that coin over, and you'll find the traits that were pushed into the shadows even though they are positive and life-promoting. These might include your assertiveness, creativity, competitiveness, or ambition. They were hidden away because they may have been seen as a threat or were simply not encouraged.

So, when we talk about shadow self-integration, we mean the process of acknowledging and embracing both sides of the coin—the parts of you that have been repressed, whether they are considered "good" or "bad" by others. It's about making peace with all these aspects, not to achieve perfection but to move toward wholeness.

Carl Jung emphasized that our goal should be to become whole, not perfect. The journey to becoming a complete and fulfilled person involves integrating these elements of our psyche that have been hidden away for too long *(How to Integrate Your Shadow—the Dark Side Is Unrealized Potential, 2020)*.

By doing so, you're not only healing the wounds caused by repressing certain traits but also unlocking your hidden potential. Your greater character, your more effective approach to life, lies in embracing your entire self. As you bring your shadow self into the light, you'll experience a profound sense of freedom and vitality that comes from living authentically *(Shadow Integration 101, 2019)*.

Integrating Shadow Work into Daily Life

Mindful Excercise: Practice It As Often As You Can

Mindfulness is a powerful tool for integrating shadow work into your daily life. It requires you to be present in the moment and notice your thoughts and emotions without judgment.

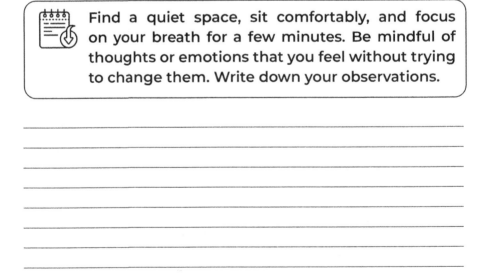

Find a quiet space, sit comfortably, and focus on your breath for a few minutes. Be mindful of thoughts or emotions that you feel without trying to change them. Write down your observations.

Exercise: Pay Attention to Your Triggers

As you move deeper into shadow work, you may uncover memories and emotions that trigger feelings of shame or discomfort. Recognizing these triggers is essential for growth.

 Use this space as a trigger journal. Whenever you experience a trigger, jot down the situation, your feelings, and any memories associated with it. This will give you the ability to notice any patterns in your shadow.

Triggers	Feelings & Memories Evoked

Exercise: Pay Attention to the Feelings in Your Body

Emotions often manifest physically. Pay attention to bodily sensations, as they can provide valuable insights into your shadow self.

 I would like you to find a spot where you feel safe and comfortable. Gently close your eyes if you are okay doing so. Next, inhale with three deep breaths and slowly scan your body from head to toe. Note any areas of tension or discomfort and record them in your workbook.

_____

_____

_____

_____

_____

 ### Exercise: Take Deep Breaths as You Process Painful Memories

When you encounter painful memories or emotions during shadow work, deep breathing can help you stay grounded and regulate your emotions.

 Create a breathing break routine. When you feel overwhelmed by difficult emotions, take a few minutes to sit quietly and focus on your breath. Inhale deeply for a count of four, hold for four, and exhale for four. Repeat until you feel more centered.

Exercise: Take Note of Thought Patterns and Habits

Shadow work often reveals recurring thought patterns and habits that have been holding you back. Identifying these is a key step in personal growth.

> **Keep a thought and habit log in your workbook. Throughout the day, jot down any thoughts or behaviors that you notice are unhelpful or self-sabotaging. This awareness will enable you to work on transforming these patterns over time.**

Negative Thoughts & Habits Log

1. _____
2. _____
3. _____
4. _____
5. _____
6. _____
7. _____
8. _____
9. _____
10. _____
11. _____
12. _____

Research has shown that incorporating mindfulness practices into daily life can lead to reduced stress, improved emotional regulation, and enhanced overall well-being (Keng et al., 2011). Additionally, studies on trauma-focused therapy emphasize the importance of recognizing triggers and addressing bodily sensations to heal from past traumatic experiences (Sweeney et al., 2018).

Sheila's Story

Sheila's life had always seemed picture-perfect on the surface. To her friends and family, she appeared confident, successful, and full of energy. However, behind her radiant smile, Sheila grappled with an overwhelming sense of anxiety, persistent guilt, and a never-ending feeling of emotional exhaustion. Every day felt like a battle, and she often found herself overwhelmed by a wide range of unwanted emotions, from anxiety and fear to deep sadness and mental exhaustion.

One evening, while scrolling through social media, Sheila came across a post about shadow work. The concept intrigued her, and as she delved into articles and videos, she realized that this might be the missing piece in her journey toward self-discovery and healing. She felt apprehensive but also curious, sensing that shadow work could provide her with the tools she needed to regain control over her emotions and life.

Sheila began her shadow work journey with cautious optimism. She started by exploring her past, reflecting on her childhood experiences and early memories. It wasn't always easy, as some of these memories were painful and brought up intense emotions. But she persevered, determined to understand the root causes of her anxiety and guilt.

As she delved deeper into her shadow, Sheila discovered triggers she hadn't recognized before. Certain situations or comments would provoke intense feelings of shame or insecurity. Instead of pushing these emotions away, she decided to confront them head-on. Sheila created a "Trigger Journal" in her shadow work workbook, noting down each trigger, the feelings it evoked, and any associated memories. This practice helped her identify patterns in her shadow self, providing valuable insights into her emotional landscape.

Sheila also paid close attention to her body's reactions during her shadow work sessions. She noticed that her shoulders would tense up, and her heart would race when she revisited painful memories. To address this, she incorporated a daily "Body Scan" practice. Sitting quietly, she closed her eyes, took deep breaths, and mentally scanned her body from head to toe. This exercise allowed her to release physical tension and remain present in the moment.

One of the most significant breakthroughs for Sheila was recognizing her recurring thought patterns and habits. Through her shadow work, she discovered that she often engaged in negative self-talk and self-sabotaging behaviors. To address this, she maintained a "Thought and Habit Log" in her workbook. Throughout the day, she recorded any detrimental thoughts or behaviors she noticed. Over time, this awareness empowered her to challenge and transform these patterns into more positive and self-affirming ones.

As months passed, Sheila's consistent commitment to shadow work and daily integration paid off. She found herself more in control of her emotions, and her anxiety and guilt began to lose their grip on her. Sheila started to experience moments of inner peace and emotional balance that she had never thought possible. Her smile became even more radiant, but this time, it was genuine and reflected the newfound authenticity and self-acceptance she had discovered through her shadow work journey.

Sheila's story serves as an inspiring example of the power of shadow work and daily integration. It's a reminder that, no matter how daunting the journey may seem, with dedication, self-compassion, and the right tools, you can find your way to a brighter, more fulfilling life.

Remember, integrating shadow work into your daily life is a gradual process. Be patient and compassionate with yourself. The more you practice these strategies and activities, the more in control you'll feel and the closer you'll get to the personal growth and self-healing you desire.

Stay committed to your journey, and the light you shed on your shadow self will illuminate a path toward a brighter, more authentic you.

Visualization

Visualization can be a potent technique in your shadow work meditation arsenal. It helps you create a safe and inviting space to connect with your inner self, and it allows you to explore your shadow without fear or judgment. Let's dive into a visualization exercise designed to help you integrate your shadow self.

 ### Exercise: Shadow Integration Visualization

Begin by finding a quiet and comfortable space where you won't be disturbed. Imagine this place as your sacred sanctuary, a safe haven where you can be yourself.

> **Before we get focused, I want you to move your thoughts to one particular area of your life where you've been struggling. This could be a recurring issue that brings you pain, anger, or sadness. Write it down. This is the shadow you'll be working with today.**

* Now, close your eyes and take three deep, slow breaths. With each breath, release any tension or apprehension you may be feeling.

* Invite your shadow to step forward into your sacred space. Pay attention to its appearance and form. It may take on a physical shape or represent itself in another way.

◆ Ask your shadow when and how it was created. Request that it shows you the moment in your life when it first emerged. Allow yourself to go back in time, even if it stirs up intense emotions.

◆ Have a conversation with your shadow. Ask it what it needs from you at this moment to facilitate growth and healing. Take mental notes of its responses; these will serve as your action items.

◆ Take a moment to express your love and gratitude to your shadow. Acknowledge the lessons it has taught you. Visualize it becoming smaller and smaller until it fits in the palm of your hand.

◆ Place your hand over your heart and feel your shadow integrating into your entire being. It's no longer a fragmented part of you but a stronger, integrated aspect.

◆ Take three more deep breaths while sitting in your sacred space. Allow this newfound integration to settle within you.

◆ When you're ready, open your eyes. Write down how you feel in the area of your life you were focusing on earlier. Do you feel more at peace, lighter, and more confident?

_____

_____

_____

_____

_____

This visualization exercise serves as a bridge between your conscious and shadow self. It helps you confront and understand the hidden aspects of yourself that have been causing emotional turmoil. By integrating your shadow self with love and acceptance, you empower yourself to move forward on your path of personal growth and healing.

Reflecting on Your Progress in Shadow Work

One of the most important aspects of shadow work is acknowledging and celebrating your progress. This is a key step to keep your motivation high and build your self-confidence. Here's how you can do it:

- **Keep a shadow work journal:**
  - Create a dedicated journal where you can document your experiences, insights, and milestones.
  - Write down moments when you confronted a shadow aspect successfully or gained a deeper understanding of yourself.

- **Set small goals:**
  - Break down your shadow work into manageable goals.
  - Celebrate each time you achieve a goal, no matter how small it may seem.

- **Reward yourself:**
  - Treat yourself to something special when you reach a significant milestone.
  - This can be as simple as enjoying your favorite meal, taking a relaxing bath, or going for a nature walk.

- **Share your achievements:**
  - Don't be shy about sharing your progress with a supportive friend or a trusted therapist.
  - Their encouragement can be a powerful motivator and reminder of how far you've come.

Dealing with Plateaus and Challenges

It's natural to encounter plateaus and challenges on your shadow work journey. These moments can be frustrating, but they are also opportunities for growth. Here's how to navigate them:

- **Accept plateaus as part of the process:**
  - Understand that plateaus are common and can be indicative of deeper work ahead.
  - Use this time to reflect and reassess your approach.
- **Don't give up when challenges arise:**
  - When you encounter difficult emotions or resistance, don't let it discourage you.
  - Take a step back, breathe, and remember that this is an essential part of your healing journey.
- **Practice self-compassion:**
  - Be gentle with yourself during challenging times.
  - Self-compassion allows you to acknowledge your struggles without self-criticism.

Adjusting Your Approach Based on Progress

As you make progress in your shadow work, it's essential to adjust your approach to ensure continued growth and healing.

◆ **Regularly review your goals:**

- Periodically revisit your initial goals and assess if they still align with your evolving understanding of yourself.

- Adjust them as needed to stay aligned with your current needs.

◆ **Expand your toolkit:**

- Explore new shadow work techniques and practices.

- Experiment with meditation, journaling, dream analysis, or therapy to deepen your self-discovery.

◆ **Celebrate your evolving self:**

- Recognize that your progress is a testament to your strength and resilience.

- Celebrate not only the changes you've made but also your willingness to grow.

◆ **Stay patient and persistent:**

- Remember that shadow work is an ongoing process.

- Embrace the journey and trust that it will lead you to a place of greater self-awareness and healing.

Interactive Element: Practical Tools For Tracking Progress

I wanted to offer five of the top tools for tracking progress while on this journey. Writing in a journal is helpful, but as busy as we can get, having an app at our disposal can be a huge help. Let's review the ones people seem to love the most:

1 Shadow work App—Apple Store:

- This dedicated app is a gem for anyone on their shadow work journey. It's designed to provide you with guidance, support, and structured exercises to help you explore and integrate your shadow aspects.

- One reviewer beautifully summed it up: "Thank you for teaching me how to come from love and not fear." This app can truly help you shift from a place of fear to one of self-compassion and love.

2 Day One Journaling App—mobile and desktop:

- If you prefer the written word, the Day One Journaling App is your perfect companion. It's not just about writing down your thoughts; it's about recording your daily reflections and insights.

- As one user passionately shared, "This is my favorite app. I use it every day if 72,000 words weren't telling enough." It's a testament to how this app can help you dig deep and discover your inner thoughts and emotions.

3 Journey: Journal App:

- Journey is more than just a journaling app; it's a holistic self-improvement tool. It offers audio options, making it accessible even on the go.

- What sets it apart is its mood-tracking feature, allowing you to monitor your emotional state throughout your shadow work journey. Additionally, you can opt into coaching programs on self-confidence, boundary setting, and mindfulness, making it an all-encompassing choice for your self-growth journey.

4 **Penzu:**

- For those concerned about privacy, Penzu is the answer. It's a secure online journaling platform available on iOS and Android. Your entries are protected with password security, ensuring your thoughts remain private.

- Customization options and the ability to add photos to your entries make Penzu suitable for recording your shadow work experiences in a visually engaging way.

5 **Evernote:**

- Evernote is a versatile note-taking app that can be easily adapted for journaling. Its cross-platform support means you can access your entries from anywhere.

- Evernote is especially helpful for shadow work because of its robust search functionality and tagging system. These features allow you to organize and easily locate your entries, making it an excellent choice for reflection and review.

Choose the tool that resonates with you the most, whether it's an app designed specifically for shadow work or a versatile journaling platform. These tools will not only help you track your progress but also provide a safe and organized space for your self-exploration journey. Remember, the journey is unique to you, and these tools are here to support you every step of the way.

In this chapter, we've explored the profound concept of shadow integration, the process of accepting and embracing your shadow side. By doing so, you've taken a courageous step to become a fully whole being, where your shadow and light coexist harmoniously.

Accepting your shadow is not about denying your light or succumbing to your darkness. It's about recognizing that you are a complex and multifaceted being. Just as the sun casts both light and shadows, so do you. When you integrate your shadow aspects, you unlock a profound sense of freedom, joy, and wholeness.

With your shadow work journey underway, you're poised to step into the next and final chapter. Here, you'll explore hope, motivation, and inspiration to continue your transformative journey. You've already come so far, and your inner light is ready to shine brighter than ever before.

Stay curious, stay compassionate, and most importantly, stay committed to your personal growth. The path ahead may have challenges, but it's also illuminated by the brilliance of your own light.

CHAPTER 8
CONSCIOUSLY LIVING IN THE LIGHT

Consciously Living in the Light

> *Your life will be transformed when you make peace with your shadow. The caterpillar will become a breathtakingly beautiful butterfly. You will no longer have to pretend to be someone you're not. You will no longer have to prove you're good enough. –* **Debbie Ford**

You've come a long way from the beginning of this workbook, and your commitment to exploring your shadow self has been truly remarkable. As we engage in this final chapter, I want you to take a moment to acknowledge the courage it took to confront your hidden aspects, the parts of yourself that you may have long ignored or denied.

In this final chapter, we'll explore what it means to consciously live in the light. It's the culmination of your efforts, the point where your shadow and your conscious self can come together in harmony. It's about applying the lessons you've learned in your daily life, using your newfound self-awareness to navigate challenges, and building a brighter, more fulfilling future.

But before we dive into the practical aspects of consciously living in the light, I want you to pause and reflect on the progress you've made. Always be mindful of your victories. Celebrate all of them. You've faced your fears, acknowledged your pain, and taken crucial steps toward self-healing and personal growth.

As you move forward, you'll continue to uncover new layers of your shadow and integrate them into your conscious self. It's a path filled with ups and downs, but each step brings you closer to a brighter, more authentic version of yourself.

So, as we embark on this final chapter, let hope, motivation, and inspiration fill your heart. You've already proven your strength and resilience, and the future holds endless possibilities for you. By consciously living in the light, you'll not only benefit yourself but also the people around you. Your newfound self-awareness will shine as a beacon of positivity, and your journey will inspire others to embark on their own path of self-discovery and healing.

When Are We Done?

So you might be wondering, "How will I know when I'm done? Is there an endpoint to this journey?" The short answer is no There's no finish line in shadow work because personal growth is an ongoing process. However, there are some clear signs that can help you recognize your progress.

 ### *Exercise: Emotional Resilience*

One significant indicator of healing your shadow is that your emotional responses become more balanced and resilient. The things that used to trigger intense reactions in you may no longer have that power. You'll notice that you can handle difficult situations with greater composure.

 Write down a list of situations, people, or events that used to trigger strong emotional reactions in you. Now, reflect on how you respond to them today.

Triggering Situations	How did you respond TODAY?

Have you noticed any changes? How do you feel about your progress?

 ## Exercise: Less Projection

When you're deep into shadow work, you often project your own unresolved issues onto others. As you heal, you'll find that you're less likely to blame or judge others for things that are actually about you. Your relationships become more harmonious and authentic.

Recall a recent conflict or disagreement you had with someone. Write down how you reacted. Were you quick to blame them, or did you pause to reflect on your own feelings and reactions? Analyze how you handled the situation and how you might approach it differently now.

Exercise: Improved Self-Awareness

The more you explore your shadow, the more you understand yourself. You become more in tune with your thoughts, emotions, and behaviors. This heightened self-awareness allows you to make conscious choices rather than reacting on autopilot.

 Keep a journal for a week where you jot down your thoughts, feelings, and actions in different situations. At the end of the week, review your journal and identify any patterns or triggers you notice. How can this awareness help you grow?

Monday

The thoughts and feelings I had today are_____

_____

_____

_____

Actions I did or didn't take today are_____

_____

_____

_____

Tuesday

The thoughts and feelings I had today are_____

_____

_____

_____

Actions I did or didn't take today are_____

_____

_____

_____

Wednesday

The thoughts and feelings I had today are_____

_____

_____

_____

Actions I did or didn't take today are_____

_____

_____

_____

Thursday

The thoughts and feelings I had today are_____

_____

_____

_____

Actions I did or didn't take today are_____

_____

_____

_____

Friday

The thoughts and feelings I had today are_____

_____

_____

_____

Actions I did or didn't take today are_____

_____

_____

_____

Saturday

The thoughts and feelings I had today are_____

_____

_____

_____

Actions I did or didn't take today are_____

_____

_____

_____

Sunday

The thoughts and feelings I had today are_____

_____

_____

_____

Actions I did or didn't take today are_____

_____

_____

_____

Review your self-awareness journal and identify any patterns or triggers you notice. How can this awareness help you grow?

_____

_____

_____

_____

_____

_____

_____

 ## *Exercise: Forgiveness and Compassion*

Healing your shadow often involves forgiving yourself for past mistakes and embracing self-compassion. When you find it easier to forgive yourself and others, it's a sign that you're making progress.

Reflect on a mistake or regret from your past. How do you feel about it now? Can you find it in yourself to forgive yourself for that moment? Write a letter of forgiveness to yourself or to someone who may have hurt you.

A study found that individuals who engage in shadow work and self-exploration report decreased levels of anxiety and depression and improved self-esteem over time (Mayer, 2023).

Mitchell's Story

Mitchell, like many of us, had his fair share of inner turmoil. He struggled with intense anxiety that often left him feeling paralyzed. Every day seemed like a battle, and he longed for a sense of control over his emotions. His heart raced, his palms sweated, and his thoughts spiraled into a never-ending loop of worry.

The idea of shadow work initially filled Mitchell with trepidation. He knew it meant delving into the depths of his psyche, confronting buried emotions, and addressing past traumas. But he also knew that something had to change. He couldn't continue to live in the shadow of his anxiety.

With determination, Mitchell took the first step on this daunting path. He committed himself to the process, understanding that it wouldn't be easy, but it was necessary for his personal growth and healing.

As the weeks turned into months, Mitchell began to notice significant changes in his life. His anxiety attacks, which used to be a daily ordeal, became less frequent and less severe. The relentless grip of fear began to loosen.

One pivotal moment occurred during a family gathering, an event that had always triggered crippling anxiety. Mitchell had a history of feeling inadequate, stemming from his childhood experiences and a deep-seated fear of abandonment.

But this time, something was different. As he stood amidst the chatter of relatives and the clinking of dishes, Mitchell felt an unexpected calm wash over him. He realized that he was no longer overwhelmed by his anxiety. The same situation that had once sent him into a panic had lost its power.

It was a powerful moment of realization. Mitchell had, through his dedicated shadow work, unearthed and confronted the roots of his anxiety. He had explored the shadows of inadequacy and the fear of abandonment that had haunted him for so long. By doing so, he had taken back control over his emotions and his life.

He realized that his triggers, which had once held him hostage, no longer had the same grip on him. It was a liberating feeling that brought tears of joy and relief to his eyes.

Mitchell's journey, much like your own, is a testament to the transformative power of shadow work. It shows that with dedication, self-compassion, and the willingness to face your inner demons, you can overcome even the most profound inner struggles.

How To Get Back On Track

Now that you have come this far in acknowledging what your shadow self is and how to integrate it, how will you know when it is taking over? What signs will show you that you're reacting or making bad decisions based on your shadow self, that part of you rooted in the past? Once you recognize this is happening, how do you change course and get back on track?

Let's review some caution signs that your shadow side may be taking over:

- **Intense emotional reactions:** Even after doing all of this work, it can be normal to find yourself experiencing strong emotions like anger, anxiety, or sadness that seem out of proportion to the situation. Just be mindful that this is your shadow self.

- **Repeated patterns:** You once again notice recurring patterns in your life, such as consistently attracting the same types of unhealthy relationships or encountering the same obstacles. After doing this work, you can recognize this is your shadow self.

- **Projection:** You might frequently find yourself once again judging or reacting strongly to certain qualities or behaviors in others. You understand now these might actually be reflections of your unacknowledged traits.

◆ **Self-sabotage:** You may engage in self-destructive behaviors or habits that hinder your personal growth, like procrastination, substance abuse, or excessive self-criticism. Be mindful that this is your shadow self.

Exercise: Shadow Self Check-In

Here are some key questions to ask yourself daily to help you gain better control over your shadow self.

> Ask yourself if this choice, decision, or reaction is helping or harming me or others. Take a moment to reflect on your decisions and actions. Write down whether they align with your values and serve your well-being. If you catch yourself acting in a way that's harmful, pause and write down why think you're making that choice.

_____
_____
_____
_____
_____
_____
_____
_____
_____
_____
_____
_____
_____
_____
_____

What emotions am I feeling, and why? Regularly check in with your emotions. Write down your answers to the following: Am I feeling angry, anxious, or sad? Try to trace these emotions back to their source. Are they linked to past experiences or suppressed feelings?

Am I projecting my own unacknowledged qualities? When you find yourself strongly reacting to someone else's behavior, consider whether you might be projecting your own suppressed traits onto them. When the situation is resolved, take some time to write down your thoughts. Were you able to see your shadow self in your reaction, and if so, how did you handle it? This awareness can help you reclaim those aspects of yourself.

Ivy's Story

Meet Ivy, a young woman who has been grappling with chronic anxiety for most of her life. She had embarked on the challenging path of shadow work, determined to unearth the buried aspects of her personality and heal her emotional wounds. As she moved into her shadow, Ivy began to discover the roots of her anxiety, which were deeply intertwined with her childhood experiences.

Ivy's shadow work was a path marked by perseverance and self-discovery. She spent countless hours in self-reflection and introspection, slowly bringing her shadow self into the light. She unearthed long-buried memories of her parents' turbulent divorce and the emotional neglect she had suffered during her formative years.

However, despite her progress, Ivy still faced moments when her past would resurface, and her anxiety would impose itself on her current relationships. It was in these moments that she would become frustrated and wonder why she had bothered with all the hard work on herself in the first place.

One day, Ivy found herself in a heated argument with her partner over something seemingly trivial. Her heart raced, her palms became sweaty, and she felt an overwhelming urge to lash out, just as she had done in the past. In that moment, Ivy's old patterns seemed to be reasserting themselves.

But Ivy had developed a set of strategies to identify her shadow self and regain her balance when such situations arose. She took a deep breath and asked herself the key questions she had learned during her shadow work journey:

 ### *"What Emotions Am I Feeling, and Why?"*

Ivy recognized that the intense anger she was experiencing was a familiar defense mechanism. It was a way her shadow self used to protect her from feeling vulnerable, just as she had felt vulnerable during her parents' divorce.

"Am I Reacting or Responding?"

She realized that she was reacting impulsively rather than responding thoughtfully. Ivy's shadow self was trying to protect her, but it was doing so in an outdated and harmful way.

 ## *"Is This Choice or Act Helping or Harming Me or Others?"*

Ivy acknowledged that her outburst was harming both her and her partner. This realization helped her step back from the brink of the argument and choose a more constructive path.

Through her shadow work, Ivy cultivated self-awareness and a toolbox of coping strategies. She knew how to recognize when her shadow self was reacting, and she had learned to respond in healthier ways. Ivy reached out to her partner, apologized for her behavior, and explained that her anxiety had momentarily taken control.

Over time, Ivy's dedication to shadow work paid off. She found herself having fewer and less intense moments of anxiety-driven reactions. Her relationships improved, and she felt a growing sense of peace within herself.

Ivy's journey was a testament to the power of shadow work and self-awareness. While her shadow self occasionally resurfaced, Ivy had the tools and resilience to navigate those moments and continue her path of healing and growth. Her story inspired others to embark on their own journey of self-discovery, knowing that transformation was possible, one step at a time.

Underlying Fear

In this section, we'll explore how fear underlies many of our unhelpful choices and thoughts. By exploring this topic, you'll gain clearer insights into your shadow self and continue the path to a life of growth and self-healing.

Fear is a primal emotion deeply ingrained in our human psyche. It's a natural response that has both a universal biochemical aspect and a highly individualized emotional component (Fritscher, 2023). Understanding fear can help us unlock the power of shadow work.

When we talk about fear, we need to understand that it is made up of two different reactions when we perceive a threat (Fritscher, 2023):

Biochemical reaction to fear: When we think there is a threat, our bodies experience a set of physical reactions. These include sweating, an increased heart rate, and a surge of adrenaline that makes us hyper-alert. This physical response is often called "fight or flight," where your body prepares itself to either confront the danger or escape from it. This reaction is a product of evolution and plays a vital role in our survival.

Emotional response to fear: The physical reaction to fear is pretty consistent among most of us, but the emotional response is highly personalized. Interestingly, fear triggers some of the same chemical reactions in our brains that positive emotions like happiness and excitement do. This is why some of us find certain fear-inducing situations exhilarating, such as jumping out of planes or axe throwing.

On the flip side, there are those who have a negative reaction to fear and actively avoid fear-inducing situations. For them, fear can be paralyzing and cause distress. The experience of fear, whether positive or negative, largely depends on the person and their life experiences.

So, how does fear play into shadow work? Well, fear often acts as a barrier that prevents us from exploring our shadow selves. It's the voice that says, "Don't go there; it's too painful" or "You're not ready to face that aspect of yourself." This fear can manifest in various ways, from self-doubt to procrastination and avoidance.

 ### *Exercise: Overcoming Fear*

 Take a moment to reflect on what specific fears might be hindering your self-discovery journey. Write them down. Awareness is the first step.

1. _____

_____

2. _____

_____

3. _____

_____

4. _____

_____

5. _____

_____

Be gentle with yourself. Recognize that fear is a natural response, and it's okay to feel it. Embrace self-compassion as you navigate your fears.

Start small. Begin with less intimidating aspects of your shadow self before delving into deeper layers. This gradual exposure can build your confidence.

Imagine a safe and nurturing space where you can explore your shadow without judgment or harm. Visualization can help you feel more at ease.

Noticing Fear

So, let's get started on understanding fear, one of the emotions that often hides in our shadows.

Fear is a powerful and complex emotion. It can manifest in various ways and often lurks beneath many of the negative feelings—anxiety, guilt, sadness, and more. By shining a light on your fears, you can start to regain control over your emotions and find a path toward healing.

Let's break down fear into some common categories and types:

◆ **Survival fear:** This is the most primal fear, rooted in our survival instincts. It includes the fear of physical harm, danger, or death. For example, fear of heights, spiders, or loud noises.

◆ **Emotional fear:** These fears are related to our emotional well-being. They can include fear of rejection, abandonment, or loneliness. Emotional fears often underlie issues like low self-esteem or social anxiety.

◆ **Fear of the unknown:** This fear revolves around uncertainty and the future. It can manifest as anxiety about what might happen, fear of change, or fear of the unfamiliar.

◆ **Fear of failure:** Many people grapple with the fear of not being good enough, fear of making mistakes, or fear of disappointing others. This fear can lead to perfectionism and self-doubt.

◆ **Fear of vulnerability:** This fear is tied to showing your true self to others. It can make you put up emotional walls, afraid of being hurt if you let people in. It often masks deeper insecurities.

Understanding the types of fear is just the first step. Now, let's explore what might be hiding beneath these fears:

- **Past trauma:** Sometimes, your fears are rooted in past traumatic experiences. They act as a defense mechanism to protect you from reliving those painful moments.

- **Limiting beliefs:** Negative beliefs about yourself or the world can fuel your fears. Identifying and challenging these beliefs is crucial for growth.

- **Unmet needs:** Fear can arise when your core emotional needs aren't being met, such as the need for love, acceptance, or safety.

- **Repressed emotions:** Fear often conceals other emotions like anger, sadness, or shame. Your shadow self might be using fear as a shield to avoid dealing with these deeper feelings.

 Fear Exercises

 Create a fear journal and write down instances when you felt afraid. Try to categorize them into the types of fear we discussed. For each fear, reflect on what might be underlying it.

Instances You Felt Afraid	Type of Fear (from the list above)	What Fuels This Fear?

Identify a fear that's been holding you back. Write down the beliefs associated with it. Are these beliefs helping or hindering your growth?

_____

_____

_____

_____

_____

_____

_____

_____

_____

Think back to a specific time when you felt intense fear. Can you recall what exactly was happening in your life at that time? Are there any unprocessed emotions or unmet needs associated with that memory?

_____

_____

_____

_____

_____

_____

_____

Recent studies have shown that acknowledging and confronting your fears can lead to reduced anxiety and improved emotional regulation (Cisler et al., 2009).

Processing Fear: Using Fear as a Catalyst for Growth

Fear is a powerful and natural emotion. It's something we all experience from time to time, and for many, it can feel overwhelming. The good news is that fear is also a valuable tool for self-discovery and growth. It's like a sign pointing to areas of your life that need your attention.

 ### *Exercise: Acknowledge Your Fear*

The first step is to recognize when you're feeling fearful. Take a moment to pause and identify the source of your fear. Is it related to a specific situation, person, or memory? Write it down in your workbook.

Create a fear journal. Write down instances when you feel fear and include any thoughts or physical sensations that accompany it.

Fear	Physical reactions

 ## Exercise: Breathe Through It

When fear grips you, focus on your breath. Deep, slow breaths can help calm your nervous system and bring you back to the present moment.

 Practice a 5-minute daily breathing exercise. Write down your experiences and any changes in your fear levels.

_____

_____

_____

_____

 ## Exercise: Question Your Fear

Ask yourself why you're feeling this fear. What's the underlying belief or thought that's causing it? Often, our fears are rooted in past experiences or limiting beliefs.

Write down three of your most common fears and the beliefs associated with them. Challenge these beliefs by seeking evidence to the contrary.

Fear #1:_____

Beliefs associated with that fear	Evidence to the contrary

Fear #2:_____

Beliefs associated with that fear	Evidence to the contrary

Fear #3:_____

Beliefs associated with that fear	Evidence to the contrary

 ### Exercise: Visualize Fear as a Teacher

Imagine fear as a wise mentor trying to teach you something important. What lessons might it have for you? This perspective can help you approach fear with curiosity rather than avoidance.

Visualize a conversation with your fear mentor and write down the lessons or insights it offers.

Strategies for Managing Fear and Anxiety

Fear is like a wall that separates you from the life you desire. If you continually avoid situations that scare you, you'll miss out on valuable experiences and opportunities for growth. Avoidance might temporarily relieve your anxiety, but it often leads to a pattern where anxiety problems intensify over time.

So, how do you break this cycle? By facing your fears head-on. Here's how:

 ### *Set Small, Achievable Goals*

Start small. Identify situations or triggers that make you anxious. Instead of diving into the deep end, set achievable goals to gradually confront your fears. This gradual approach allows you to build confidence and realize that the situation might not be as bad as you expect.

 ### *Exercise: Get to Know Your Fear*

Understanding your fear is essential. Keep an anxiety diary to track your emotions, triggers, and physical sensations when anxiety strikes. This self-awareness will empower you to manage your feelings better.

Create a list of things that help you cope during anxious moments. This list can be a powerful tool for addressing the underlying beliefs that fuel your anxiety.

1. _____
2. _____
3. _____
4. _____
5. _____
6. _____
7. _____
8. _____
9. _____
10. _____

Share with a Trusted Friend or Family Member

It's common to feel ashamed or silly about your fears and anxieties, but you don't have to face them alone. If you have a trusted friend or family member, confide in them. Talking about your fears can reduce anxiety levels and pave the way for additional support if needed.

Embrace Physical Activity

Exercise is a fantastic way to distract your mind from fear and anxiety. You don't need to run a marathon; even gentle stretches, seated exercises, or a leisurely walk can work wonders. Exercise releases endorphins, the body's natural mood lifters, which can help improve your emotional state.

 Write down three ways you feel you can move your body.

1. _____
2. _____
3. _____

Relaxation Techniques

Learning relaxation techniques can help you combat both the mental and physical aspects of fear. Simple practices like deep breathing, envisioning a calming place, or exploring complementary therapies such as massage, yoga, mindfulness, and meditation can provide significant relief.

> Write down three relaxation techniques you believe you can adapt to your daily life.

1. _____
2. _____
3. _____

Nurture Your Body

Your diet can influence anxiety levels. Consume plenty of fruits and vegetables while limiting sugar intake to prevent blood sugar spikes. Minimize your caffeine consumption by reducing tea and coffee, as caffeine can exacerbate anxiety.

> Jot down three things you can do to change your diet to improve your anxiety levels.

1. _____
2. _____
3. _____

Moderate Alcohol Intake

Although some might call it courage, alcohol isn't your ally in managing fear and anxiety. It can intensify anxious feelings and lead to more significant emotional struggles. If you do drink, do so in moderation.

These practical strategies, when combined with self-awareness and the willingness to face your fears, can be powerful tools for managing anxiety and fear as you embark on your shadow work journey.

Jaime's Story

Jaime, much like many of us, faced a constant battle with anxiety and fear. However, instead of confronting these emotions, she turned to unhealthy coping mechanisms to find temporary relief. For instance:

- **Anxiety at bedtime:** When the anxiety struck at bedtime, Jaime would reach for a glass, or sometimes three, to help her fall asleep. This reliance on alcohol as a crutch only masked her anxiety temporarily and created a vicious cycle.

- **Fear of confrontation at work:** At her job, Jaime had a deep-seated fear of confrontation. This fear held her back from addressing issues and voicing her opinions, even when it meant missing out on significant advancement opportunities. Her avoidance strategy kept her stuck in a job she didn't truly love.

One day, Jaime decided she couldn't continue down this path of self-doubt and anxiety-driven choices. She realized that in order to truly grow and find inner peace, she needed to confront her fears head-on.

Instead of reaching for a glass of alcohol when bedtime anxiety hit, Jaime started practicing relaxation techniques. She used deep breathing exercises and guided imagery to calm her mind. Over time, these techniques became her new bedtime routine, gradually reducing her reliance on alcohol.

Jaime decided to tackle her fear of confrontation at work. She began by setting small, achievable goals. She started by speaking up in team meetings and gradually worked her way up to addressing larger issues. As she saw positive outcomes and received support from colleagues, her confidence grew.

Alongside these changes, Jaime made healthier choices in her life. She started eating better, incorporating more fruits and vegetables into her diet, and reducing her sugar intake. She also decided to drink alcohol in moderation and found that she felt more in control of her emotions as a result.

As Jaime continued to face her fears and adopt healthier coping strategies, her life began to transform. She gained a newfound sense of confidence and self-assuredness. Her relationships improved, both personally and professionally, as she learned to communicate effectively and assertively. Most importantly, Jaime found inner peace that had eluded her for years.

Jaime's journey shows us that with determination, self-awareness, and a willingness to confront our fears, we can break free from the shackles of anxiety and fear. As you embark on your own shadow work, remember that you have the power to transform your life, just like Jaime did. It's a journey of self-discovery and healing, and you're taking the first steps toward a brighter, more peaceful future.

The Antidote to Fear is not Courage—It's Love

In this section, we'll explore a profound truth: the antidote to fear is not courage—it is love. Fear can be an overwhelming and paralyzing emotion, and you've likely felt its grip on your life in various forms.

Let's begin by delving into exercises that will help you embrace the power of love to overcome fear and take charge of your emotional well-being.

Exercise: Self-Compassion

 Write down a list of encouraging and comforting statements about yourself. This is to remind you of your worth. You deserve love and understanding.

1. _____
2. _____
3. _____
4. _____
5. _____
6. _____
7. _____
8. _____
9. _____
10. _____

List three things you are grateful for. Gratitude can shift your focus from fear to love and abundance.

1. _____
2. _____
3. _____

Write down three self-care routines that you can use to nurture your body and soul. Whether it's taking a long bath, going for a walk in nature, or simply enjoying a cup of tea, prioritize activities that bring you joy and peace.

1. _____
2. _____
3. _____

Staying Motivated in Your Shadow Work Journey

Motivation fuels your commitment and helps you navigate the challenging moments that will inevitably arise. It's the driving force behind your transformation. Let's review some exercises to help you stay motivated as you continue your shadow work journey.

 ## *Exercise: Connect with Nature*

Nature can be a powerful ally in your shadow work journey. Spend time outdoors, whether it's a walk in the park, a hike in the woods, or simply sitting in your backyard. Nature has a way of grounding us and providing clarity.

 Dedicate at least 30 minutes each day to connect with nature. Write down your feelings and thoughts during these moments.

Thoughts on Nature Walk #1

_____

_____

_____

_____

_____

Thoughts on Nature Walk #2

_____

_____

_____

_____

_____

Thoughts on Nature Walk #3

_____

_____

_____

_____

_____

 Exercise: Explore Creative Expression

Art, writing, music, and other forms of creative expression can be therapeutic. Engage in creative activities that allow you to explore your emotions and experiences in a non-judgmental way.

 Start an art journal, write poetry, or create a playlist of songs that resonate with your journey. Use these outlets to express yourself freely.

Exercise: Seek Guidance from Dreams

Our dreams often hold valuable insights. Keep a dream journal by your bedside and jot down your dreams upon waking. Over time, patterns and symbols may emerge that shed light on your shadow.

 Start a dream journal and record your dreams regularly. Look for recurring themes or symbols and contemplate their significance.

 ## *Exercise: Vision Board*

I want to invite you to create a vision board for your future growth and the life you want.

I would like you to take a few moments to really think about your intentions. Consider the aspects of your shadow self that you want to envision for yourself in the future.

 Write down your intentions in a clear and concise manner. For example, "I intend to explore and heal my suppressed emotions, fears, and limiting beliefs while manifesting a brighter, more authentic future."

_____

_____

_____

_____

Gather the materials you'll need for your vision board:

- Poster board or a large piece of cardboard.

- Scissors.

- Glue or adhesive.

- Magazines, images, and words that resonate with both your shadow work and your desired future.

- Markers, colored pencils, or other art supplies (optional).

Start flipping through magazines, books, or online resources to find images and words that resonate with both your shadow self and your vision for the future. Look for pictures that represent your suppressed emotions, fears, or the aspects of yourself you want to continue to work on. Additionally, find images and words that symbolize the positive changes and growth you want to achieve.

Now, it's time to assemble your vision board:

- Cut out the images and words that you've selected.

- Arrange them on your poster board in a way that feels visually appealing and meaningful to you. You can create sections or clusters to represent different aspects of your journey.

- Start gluing the images and words onto the poster board. As you do this, reflect on the significance of each item and how it relates to your shadow work and your desired future.

- You can get creative by adding colors, drawings, or personal touches that enhance the board's emotional resonance.

Once your vision board is complete, take some time to sit with it. Close your eyes, take a few deep breaths, and meditate on the images and words you've chosen. Allow yourself to connect with the emotions and intentions you've set for your shadow work and your future growth.

Place your vision board in a prominent and visible location where you'll see it daily. This serves as a powerful reminder of your intentions and can help keep you focused and motivated on your shadow work and your journey toward personal growth and healing.

In this chapter, we covered a great deal of fear, anxiety, hope, and motivation. As we conclude this last chapter, I want to remind you that the journey of shadow work is not always easy, but it is undeniably worth it. You have the tools to do the work, and now you know how to stay on track.

Unveiling The Shadows: A Call To Share Your Journey

In the realm of shadow work, solidarity and understanding are invaluable treasures. When you leave a review, you send an echo of support into the void, letting others know that their struggles and victories are acknowledged and shared. This sense of community is vital in a journey that can often feel isolating.

So, I call upon you, brave navigators of the inner self, to share your journey, to leave a review for this self-guided shadow work workbook and journal for beginners. Let your voice be heard, your journey acknowledged, and your wisdom shared. In doing so, you not only affirm your growth and transformation but also extend a hand to those still navigating their way through the shadows.

YOU CAN HELP OTHERS!

Thank you so much for your support. We all need a helping hand from time to time and your words could be the spark that ignites someone's transformation.

Scan the QR code to leave a quick review.

Conclusion

As we come to the end of this workbook, I want to remind you of the incredible journey you've embarked upon. Throughout these pages, you've ventured deep into the realm of shadow work, bravely confronting the shadows that have silently haunted you for so long. You've walked through the corridors of your past, where painful memories lurked, faced the storm of challenging emotions, and challenged the limitations of your beliefs with courage and unwavering determination. It's been an incredible journey, and now, it's time to distill the essence of what you've learned.

In this process, you've discovered a profound truth—your shadows are not your adversaries; they are an integral part of you. By acknowledging, embracing, and owning them, you are taking control of your own healing and personal growth. They are not your enemies, but rather, they are the stepping stones toward your wholeness.

Remember Liz, whom we met at the beginning of this workbook? Her story may resonate with the struggles you've encountered on your own path. Liz, much like you, found herself stuck in a relentless cycle of pain and confusion. She, too, harbored doubts and fears about embarking on the journey of shadow work, worrying that it might exacerbate her already heavy burdens. With courage, she took that leap of faith, just as you have. And as she progressed down this path, she started to notice the subtle but profound shifts in her life.

The heavy burden of her past began to lift, layer by layer, revealing the light that was hidden beneath. She realized that she could navigate this transformative journey at her own pace, forging her own support system along the way. Her story is a testament to the power of shadow work to bring about positive change, even in the face of doubt and fear.

Now, it's your turn to celebrate your progress. Take a moment to look back on the breakthroughs you've achieved, no matter how seemingly insignificant they may appear. Every step you've taken, every shadow you've confronted, has propelled you forward on your path to healing and self-discovery.

Share your newfound wisdom and awareness with others who may be on a similar journey. Offer them guidance, support, and encouragement, just as you've received along the way. Remember that personal growth is not a destination but a lifelong journey, and every effort you make to heal is a significant victory in itself.

If you found this workbook helpful on your journey, I invite you to consider leaving a review or sharing your experiences with others. By doing so, you can help ensure that this workbook reaches the hands of those just beginning their own path of shadow work. Your words may be the very encouragement someone else needs to take that courageous step forward in their healing journey.

So, continue to shine your light brightly, moving forward into the life you are so inherently worthy of. Your journey is a testament to your inner strength and resilience. Each new day brings you closer to a brighter, more authentic life. Thank you for allowing me to be a part of your shadow work journey, and may your path be forever illuminated with growth, healing, and love.

Other Books You'll Love By
Leigh W. Hart

Don't Get Derailed By Your Attachment Style

Whether you are anxious, avoidant, or fearful in relationships, this book will provide you with proven strategies for effectively dealing with an insecure attachment style.

 #1 Best Seller

Reparenting Your Wounded Inner Child

Explore Childhood and Generational Trauma to Break Destructive Patterns, Build Emotional Strength and Achieve Personal Growth with 7 Empowering Steps. Free yourself from the pains of the past and create a life you will love now and in the future.

CBT Inner Child Workbook

Available Fall 2024

Heal Past Trauma, Restore Emotional Resilience, and Reclaim Your Joy with Cognitive Behavioral Therapy Exercises, Journal Prompts, and Self-love Practices. This workbook is your companion on the journey to nurture and heal your inner child.

Amazon.com/Author/LeighWHart

Elevate Your Journey...

with BONUS
Complimentary Support Materials

GIFT #1: Self-Assessment Tests, Printable Affirmations & Bonus Materials

As you begin your shadow work journey, are you unsure where to focus your efforts? Use the self-assessment tests to determine which areas of your life need the most attention.

GIFT #2: The Self-Discovery Workbook

Personal growth is a lifelong journey. Use this workbook now and in the future to revisit insights learned, reevaluate your progress, and continue evolving on your path to personal fulfillment.

GIFT #3: The Evolving Growth Workbook

Personal growth is a lifelong journey. Use this workbook now and in the future to revisit insights learned, reevaluate your progress, and continue evolving on your path to personal fulfillment.

Go to:
Shadow.LeighWHart.com
to receive your BONUS printable support materials.

My GIFT to you!

References

Ackerman, C. (2019, June 21). What is self-regulation? (+95 skills and strategies). PositivePsychology.com. https://positivepsychology.com/self-regulation/

Akbari, K. (2023, July 18). Shadow work prompts for insecurity. Eye Mind Spirit. https://www.eyemindspirit.com/post/shadow-work-prompts-for-insecurity

Anderson, O. (n.d.). Oli Anderson quotes. Goodreads. https://www.goodreads.com/work/quotes/85809606-shadow-life-freedom-from-an-unreal-world---reclaim-your-hidden-self-pr#:~:text=Shadow%20Life%3A%20Freedom%20from%20an,World%20%2D%20Reclaim%20Your...&text=Your%20Shadow%20is%20all%20of,forgot%20that%20you're%20wearing.

BetterHelp Editorial Team. (2023, October 10). Introspection guide. Betterhelp. https://www.betterhelp.com/advice/psychologists/what-is-introspection-psychology-definition-and-applications/

Britt Jr, W. B. (2019, October 23). Roleplaying as shadow work. Medium. https://medium.com/@wendell.britt/roleplaying-as-shadow-work-34a072b47da9

Brown, B. (2022, December 5). What is the shadow self + shadow work. Modern Manifestation. https://www.themodernmanifestation.com/post/shadow-work

Cisler, J. M., Olatunji, B. O., Feldner, M. T., & Forsyth, J. P. (2009). Emotion regulation and the anxiety disorders: An integrative review. Journal of Psychopathology and Behavioral Assessment, 32(1), 68–82. https://doi.org/10.1007/s10862-009-9161-1

El Gerbi, Y. (2020, September 2). How I met my shadow self, and how you can meet yours. Curious. https://medium. com/curious/how-i-met-my-shadow-self-and-how-you-can-meet-yours-aea21680c7ff

Ford, D. (n.d.). Debbie Ford quotes. Goodreads. https://www. goodreads.com/author/quotes/7851.Debbie_Ford

For those who have actively engaged in shadow work, what did your process look like? I've read enough theory, and I would like to hear fr... (2021). Quora. https://www.quora. com/For-those-who-have-actively-engaged-in-shadow-work-what-did-your-process-look-like-Ive-read-enough-theory-and-I-would-like-to-hear-from-someone-who-successfully-integrated-their-shadow-in-tangible-reality-and-is-no

Fosu, K. (2020, December 14). Shadow work: A simple guide to transcending the darker aspects of the self. Medium. https://medium.com/big-self-society/shadow-work-a-simple-guide-to-transcending-the-darker-aspects-of-the-self-e948ee285723

Fritscher, L. (2023, April 11). The psychology of fear. Verywell Mind. https://www.verywellmind.com/the-psychology-of-fear-2671696

Graham, S. (n.d.). Sasha Graham quotes. Goodreads. https:// www.goodreads.com/quotes/10314300-the-shadow-is-needed-now-more-than-ever-we-heal

Griffiths, N. (2021, September 15). 40 powerful affirmations for shadow work. Seeking Serotonin. https:// seekingserotonin.com/affirmations-for-shadow-work/#google_vignette

Grinspoon, P. (2022, May 4). How to recognize and tame your cognitive distortions. Harvard Health. https://www. health.harvard.edu/blog/how-to-recognize-and-tame-your-cognitive-distortions-202205042738

Guil, R., Gómez-Molinero, R., Merchán-Clavellino, A., & Gil-Olarte, P. (2021). Lights and shadows of trait emotional intelligence: Its mediating role in the relationship between negative affect and state anxiety in university students. Frontiers in Psychology, 11. https://doi.org/10.3389/fpsyg.2020.615010

How to integrate your shadow – the dark side is unrealized potential. (2020, February 27). Academy of Ideas. https://academyofideas.com/2020/02/how-to-integrate-your-shadow/

Identifying triggers worksheet & example. (2023). Carepatron. https://www.carepatron.com/templates/identifying-triggers-worksheet

Ingram, J. (2022, May 9). Cost remains significant barrier to therapy access, Verywell Mind survey finds. Verywell Mind. https://www.verywellmind.com/cost-of-therapy-survey-5271327

Keng, S. L., Smoski, M. J., & Robins, C. J. (2011). Effects of mindfulness on psychological health: A review of empirical studies. Clinical Psychology Review, 31(6), 1041–1056. https://doi.org/10.1016/j.cpr.2011.04.006

LaVine, R. (2023, March 28). 100+ deep shadow work prompts to accept yourself and move forward. Science of People. https://www.scienceofpeople.com/shadow-work-prompts/

Mani, M. (2017, September 28). 12 short stories on self realization and finding your true self. OutofStress. https://www.outofstress.com/self-realization-short-stories/

Mayer, B. A. (2023, October 10). Shadow work: Can TikTok's self-care trend improve your mental health? Healthline. https://www.healthline.com/health-news/how-the-shadow-work-tiktok-trend-can-help-your-mental-health

Margery, M. (2023, February 2). Unless you learn to face your own shadow. The Minds Journal. https://themindsjournal.com/quotes/unless-learn-face-shadow/

Othon, J. (2017, October 20). Carl Jung and the shadow: The ultimate guide to the human dark side. HighExistence. https://www.highexistence.com/carl-jung-shadow-guide-unconscious/

Pedersen, T. (2022, May 6). 7 tips for improving your self-awareness. Psych Central. https://psychcentral.com/health/how-to-be-more-self-aware-and-why-its-important

Projection. (2022, January 5). Psychology Today. https://www.psychologytoday.com/ca/basics/projection

Regan, S. (2021, November 11). How to embrace & integrate your shadow self for major healing. Mindbodygreen. https://www.mindbodygreen.com/articles/shadow-self

"Safe place" relaxation exercise. (2019, October 30). Spring Psychology. https://www.springpsychology.co.uk/post/safe-place-relaxation-exercise

St. Catherine of Siena. (n.d.). St. Catherine of Siena quotes. AZ Quotes. https://www.azquotes.com/quote/818366

Sansone, R. A., Leung, J. S., & Wiederman, M. W. (2012). Five forms of childhood trauma. The Primary Care Companion for CNS Disorders, 14. https://doi.org/10.4088/pcc.12m01353

7 ways to spot your shadow self - inner shadow work. (2021, July 17). Inner Shadow Work. https://innershadowwork.com/7-ways-to-spot-your-shadow-self-2/

Shadow integration 101. (2019, April 3). The Lovett Center. https://thelovettcenter.com/shadow-integration-101/

Stutz, P. (2022, November 7). How to bond with your shadow. THE TOOLS. https://www.thetoolsbook.com/blog/how-to-bond-with-your-shadow

Sweeney, A., Filson, B., Kennedy, A., Collinson, L., & Gillard, S. (2018). A paradigm shift: relationships in trauma-informed mental health services. BJPsych Advances, 24(5), 319–333. https://doi.org/10.1192/bja.2018.29

Tagore, R. (n.d.). Rabindranath Tagore quotes. Goodreads. https://www.goodreads.com/work/quotes/2676430-stray-birds

Taibbi, R. (2023, August 4). How to be your own therapist. Psychology Today. https://www.psychologytoday.com/za/blog/fixing-families/202308/how-to-be-your-own-therapist

Tartakovsky, M. (2014, September 22). Embracing your dark side. Psych Central. https://psychcentral.com/blog/owning-our-dark-sides#benefits

Thakur, P. (2019, June 19). Top 10 inspirational success stories. YourStory.com. https://yourstory.com/mystory/top-10-inspirational-success-stories

Tracking progress in therapy matters (and how to do it). (2023, October 17). Www.sondermind.com. https://www.sondermind.com/resources/why-tracking-your-therapy-progress-matters-and-how-to-do-it

Veazey, K. (2022, May 3). Emotional self-regulation: Importance, problems, and strategies. MedicalNewsToday. https://www.medicalnewstoday.com/articles/emotional-self-regulation

Villines, Z. (2022, August 30). What is shadow work? Benefits and exercises. MedicalNewsToday. https://www.medicalnewstoday.com/articles/what-is-shadow-work#:~:text=Shadow%20work%20is%20a%20type

Images

Images on the following pages were created with the assistance of DALL-E 2: 19, 21, 26, 33, 52, 95, 113, 121, 137, 141

Images on the following pages were created with the assistance of Midjourney: 12, 34, 36, 39, 43, 47, 64, 66, 76, 87, 103, 106, 167, 191, 209

Advanced Self-Guided Shadow Work

A WORKBOOK and JOURNAL for
Deep Sub-Conscious Exploration,
Emotional Mastery,
and Cognitive Reframing

LEIGH W. HART

4 0 1
–Publishing–

Introduction

Welcome, my fellow seeker of self-discovery and healing, to this advanced workbook and journal for deep subconscious exploration, emotional mastery, and cognitive reframing. I commend you for the remarkable path you've chosen since delving into foundational shadow work. Your commitment to self-improvement has undoubtedly brought you profound insights and growth.

You may have already familiarized yourself with the concepts of the shadow and shadow work in my first book, Self-Guided Shadow Work for Beginners. In it, I introduced you to the notion that within each of us exists a realm of hidden thoughts, feelings, and experiences, often suppressed or denied, which influence our behavior and emotions. Shadow work is the process of unveiling and understanding this inner realm to promote personal growth and healing.

Since starting your shadow work, you've likely experienced moments of illumination and transformation. Perhaps you've uncovered hidden patterns, confronted long-buried emotions, and taken significant strides toward self-awareness. But now, you find yourself at a crossroads, having used the current methods and feeling the need for more. You're no longer content with merely managing your feelings; you yearn to unearth their roots and transform them into sources of strength and wisdom.

Beneath your pursuit of growth is a profound, often unvoiced desire for absolute emotional autonomy and self-governance. You want a life where your choices are fully conscious and aligned with your true happiness and success. The journey will involve more than coping; it's about addressing and healing the deep-seated wounds that have shaped your life so far.

You may remember Christine from my first book, but allow me to introduce you to her on a deeper level. Today, she stands as a strong, independent, funny, and confident wife and mother at the age of 51. To know her past, however, is to peer into the depths of a traumatic and toxic childhood that defies belief.

Christine's journey began in the shadowed corners of her earliest memories. She was an incest survivor, subjected to unspeakable abuse by both her grandfathers and her father until the age of ten. In the twisted tapestry of her upbringing, her narcissistic mother played a leading role, blaming Christine for the horrors inflicted upon her.

Growing up in such an environment, it's a wonder she found her way at all. Her mother relentlessly drilled into her the idea that family was everything. They would attend Christine's birthday parties and be there for her graduations, and with each passing moment, her own identity seemed to evaporate.

But the turning point in Christine's life came when she became a mother herself. Fueled by an unshakeable desire to protect her own children from the horrors she had endured, she began to dig deep into her own behaviors. Why was she so perpetually angry? Why couldn't she commit to anything, constantly hovering in a state of anxiety and control?

The quest for answers propelled her into a decade-long journey of self-discovery and shadow work. She knew the only way to truly protect her children was to first understand and heal herself. And so, Christine embarked on a profound odyssey into the recesses of her psyche, determined to reclaim her life.

Acknowledging those dark corners of her soul meant reliving the traumatic moments that had haunted her for years. It meant summoning the strength to forgive those who had caused her pain for her sake and learning to listen to the fragile voice of her inner child, the part of her that had longed for protection and care.

It wasn't an easy path. It took years of dedication, revisiting painful memories, confronting her deepest fears, and gifting herself the love and understanding she had always deserved. But gradually, Christine began to emerge as a person she didn't even know existed.

What she discovered was nothing short of miraculous. She found peace where she once believed chaos was her destiny. She discovered calm where she had once been overwhelmed by anxiety. And most importantly, she unearthed a wellspring of joy within herself that she had never known was possible.

Christine didn't always know that this kind of life existed. She had been convinced that her path was forever marked by chaos, tragedy, and unhappiness. But today, she shares her story with the world to offer hope to others trapped in their shadows.

She wants you to know that if you commit yourself to illuminating those dark places within and are willing to do the hard work of shadow exploration, you can light your own path and find your way to a life that is truly yours. Christine's journey is a testament to the resilience of the human spirit and the transformative power of shadow work. It's a story of reclamation, healing, and the unwavering belief that the light can always pierce through the darkest shadows.

This workbook is designed to guide you on this daring expedition into the depths of your psyche. It goes beyond the basics, offering advanced techniques and exercises for deep psychological healing and long-term emotional resilience. It aims to empower you to identify the root causes of your recurring patterns and provide practical steps to create new, healthy habits that align with your desired life trajectory.

So, why is it beneficial and necessary to delve deeper? Basic techniques can be likened to laying the foundation of a house. They provide stability and structure but leave the rooms empty. Advanced shadow work is about furnishing those rooms, making them spaces of comfort and growth, and transforming your entire dwelling into a sanctuary of self-discovery and healing.

Before we dive into the advanced exercises and insights to come, let's take a moment to reflect on your progress and any challenges you've faced since you started your journey. I want you to acknowledge your growth, no matter how small it may seem, for it is the foundation upon which we will build. Be proud of that.

Creating the right environment for this work is essential. The space you choose for healing should be clutter-free and calm. As you embark on this transformative journey, consider the following tips to make your home a sanctuary for your healing process:

- ⊘ Surround yourself with nature. If you can, have access to a view of the outdoors. Decorate with your favorite plants or flowers. Get creative with artwork depicting nature scenes that make you feel calm. Don't forget the impact of natural light.

- ⊘ Decorate with meaning. Sit in this space each time you add something. Ask yourself if that item has meaning to you. For instance, in my space, I have a small trinket box given to me by my grandmother. She was a strong woman, and she inspired me. It could be as simple as a picture you found in a magazine.

- ⊘ Simplify your life. You should keep this space clutter-free. Your mind will work best this way. Do your best to keep it clean of dust, trash, and anything that doesn't need to be in there. Think of it as a clean slate.

- ⊘ Choose the right colors. This is specific to you. What colors calm you? What colors motivate you? For instance, blues, greens, and light purple tend to evoke calm. Choose those colors that resonate with you.

Remember, your external environment has a profound impact on your internal well-being. Take these steps to create a harmonious space that supports your healing journey.

Now, let us reaffirm your commitment to self-healing. This journey requires more than a one-time decision; it demands a continual reaffirmation of your dedication to delving deeper into your own psyche and embracing the challenges that come with it. Repeat after me:

"I am worthy of this journey into self-healing."

This creed is a powerful affirmation that speaks to your inner strength and determination. Use it as a touchstone for your dedication, repeating it every morning or before engaging in the exercises within this book. Write it down, place it somewhere visible, or even memorize it as a mantra for moments when your resolve might waver. Understand that commitment is an ongoing choice, one that is reaffirmed through consistent action and reflection.

As we embark on this advanced journey of shadow work together, know that such affirmations are an integral part of your healing and growth. They serve as the beacon guiding you through the depths of your subconscious toward the light of self-awareness and transformation.

In the chapters that follow, we will explore advanced exercises, insights, and techniques that will empower you to navigate your inner landscape with courage and wisdom. I encourage you to embrace this path with an open heart and a curious mind, for within you lies the potential for profound transformation and the healing you are worthy of.

Stay committed, stay open, and remember that your path to emotional autonomy and self-governance is a testament to your resilience and determination. The transformative power you seek resides within you, waiting to be unlocked.

With warmth, empathy, and unwavering support on this journey,

Leigh

CHAPTER 1
THE DEEP DIVE

The Deep Dive

In this chapter, we start on a quest, one that explores the depths of your subconscious mind, the uncharted territory where the roots of your thoughts, feelings, and behaviors lie hidden. It's a terrain where emotions don't just echo but reverberate with the intensity of a symphony, where past experiences, traumas, and beliefs have been shaping your reality for years, often without your conscious awareness.

The essence of this chapter lies in the revelation of the significance of subconscious awareness in personal transformation. Together, we will move beyond the shallows of self-reflection into the profound depths of self-understanding. Here, you'll discover the innermost drives and fears that have been shaping your existence, often hidden from your conscious mind.

Unveiling the Subconscious

Picture this: you're learning to swim for the first time. The initial attempts are awkward, and it takes immense concentration to stay afloat. Now, fast forward to the moment you can effortlessly glide through the water. What happened in between?

This transformation, from a conscious effort to effortless mastery, is orchestrated by the subconscious mind. It's like an invisible partner in your life, constantly working behind the scenes to make things easier, more efficient, and automatic.

The subconscious mind is a component of the human mind that operates below the level of conscious awareness. It encompasses a vast reservoir of thoughts, feelings, memories, beliefs, and automatic processes that influence our thoughts, behaviors, and emotions without us being consciously aware of them. The subconscious mind plays a significant role in shaping our perceptions, decisions, and reactions, often based on past experiences and deeply ingrained patterns. It can be thought of as the hidden part of the mind that exerts a powerful influence on our daily lives, even though we may not be consciously aware of its workings *(What Is the Subconscious Mind?, 2020)*.

 ### *Power of the Subconscious Mind*

To truly appreciate its power, let's draw from some well-established psychological theories and research:

Carl Jung's Collective Unconscious Theory

Jung believed that our minds shared a collective reservoir of experiences and memories common to all humans. This collective unconscious influences our thoughts, dreams, and even symbols. For example, the archetype of a hero transcends cultures because it's deeply embedded in our collective unconscious (Fritscher, 2023).

Freud's Theory of the Subconscious Mind

Sigmund Freud proposed a theory that positioned human behavior and personality as outcomes of perpetual and distinct interplays among conflicting psychological forces operating on three different levels of awareness: the preconscious, conscious, and unconscious minds. He contended that each of these facets of the mind holds a vital role in shaping behavior.

These levels of the mind are delineated as follows:

1. The preconscious encompasses all that is potentially accessible to conscious awareness, including thoughts and memories that can be readily brought into the forefront of the conscious mind.

2. The conscious mind encapsulates the entirety of thoughts, memories, feelings, and desires that we are cognizant of at any given moment. It constitutes the facet of our mental processing that we can rationally deliberate upon and articulate. This sphere also encompasses our memory, which is not consistently within consciousness but can be easily retrieved and elevated into awareness.

3. The unconscious mind acts as a reservoir for feelings, thoughts, impulses, and recollections that elude conscious awareness. It harbors content that is often deemed unacceptable or distressing, such as sensations of pain, anxiety, or inner conflict. These elements operate beneath the surface of conscious thought, exerting a profound influence on our behaviors and emotions.

Sigmund Freud introduced the concept of the iceberg model, where the conscious mind is the tip above water, and the subconscious is the vast bulk beneath. He argued that unresolved conflicts, desires, and traumatic experiences are stored in the subconscious, impacting our behavior and emotional responses (Cherry, 2023).

John Bowlby and Attachment Theory

Attachment theory, introduced by John Bowlby, explores how early relationships with caregivers shape our subconscious beliefs about relationships and self-worth. It impacts our adult relationships and emotional responses.

We often feel the impact of these early experiences deep within our subconscious. Consequently, we may not even be fully conscious of how they subtly influence our thoughts, emotions, and behaviors in our adult relationships. Our brains have stored these early patterns as concealed implicit memories, which can clandestinely affect our attachment styles, conflict resolution aptitude, trust levels, and the overall dynamics of our relationships.

By becoming conscious of these subtle patterns and recognizing how they influence our romantic connections, we can actively take steps to challenge and transform them. Once we gain understanding, we become more attuned to our patterns and can make deliberate choices.

If you're interested in delving deeper into attachment theory, you might want to check out my first book, Don't Get Derailed By Your Attachment Style, for actionable steps on healing an insecure attachment style.

The Impact of Revealing Subconscious Thoughts

Now, let's look at the profound impact of unveiling subconscious thoughts with a real-world example—the Zaltman Metaphor Elicitation Technique (ZMET) used in marketing (Mahoney, 2003).

Imagine a company trying to understand why people choose one brand of soda over another. Traditional surveys might yield rational answers like taste or price. However, when ZMET is used, participants are asked to create collages or visual representations of their feelings about soda brands.

What emerges are rich, metaphorical images that reveal deep-seated emotions and associations with the product. Some might depict soda as a gateway to happiness, while others might show it as a source of nostalgia. These images go beyond surface-level preferences, tapping into the subconscious and unveiling the true motivations behind consumer choices.

Similarly, in your personal journey, unveiling your subconscious thoughts and beliefs is vital. It allows you to understand why you react the way you do in certain situations, why you have recurring patterns in your life, and why you might be holding yourself back from achieving your full potential—why you struggle to fully heal.

In the upcoming sections of this workbook, we'll explore advanced techniques and exercises to help you uncover, understand, and transform your subconscious mind.

Exercise: The Ultimate Self-Alignment

Imagine your perfect day, but not just any day—your ideal day five years from now. Visualize every detail, from the moment you wake up to when you go to bed.

 Describe this day in 3-5 sentences, vividly capturing the sights, sounds, smells, emotions, and interactions that make it perfect for you. Imagine the career you're in, the relationships you have, the place you live, and the person you've become.

Day 1 - Perfect Day Description - Five Years from Now

_____
_____
_____
_____
_____

Now that you've written down your vision, commit to repeating this exercise for the next 90 days. Yes, 90 days of reaffirming your true desires.

Each day for 90 days, take a few moments to revisit and refine your perfect day description. As you do this, write down any resistance or discomfort that arises.

Day 2 - Perfect Day Description - Five Years from Now

_____
_____
_____
_____
_____

Resistance or Discomfort that Arises

_____

_____

_____

_____

_____

Use a journal or notebook to repeat your perfect day description for 90 days using the above prompt to identify any progress or resistance. If you find that you're struggling to continue writing down your vision over the 90-day period, it's a clear sign that your conscious and subconscious minds may not be in alignment.

Ask yourself if the stated outcome truly resonates with your deepest desires or if it's influenced by external expectations or past conditioning.

If you discover that your initial vision wasn't entirely honest or aligned with your true self, don't worry. This is a common realization on the journey to self-discovery and healing.

Pivot. Shift your vision to one that is more authentic and in harmony with your heart's true healing path. Rewrite your perfect day description accordingly.

Self-Reflection: Beyond the Surface

Superficial self-reflection often involves skimming the surface of our thoughts, emotions, and behaviors. While it's a good starting point, it only scratches the surface of our true selves. It's like trying to understand the entire ocean by examining a single wave. To truly know ourselves and create lasting change, we need to dive deeper.

Why go deeper:

⊘ **Authenticity:** Superficial self-reflection may lead to superficial change. To authentically transform our lives, we must explore the root causes of our patterns and reactions.

⊘ **Emotional resilience:** Deeper self-reflection empowers us to face and heal the wounds that underlie our emotional reactions. This builds emotional resilience, making us better equipped to navigate life's challenges.

⊘ **Freedom from repetition:** Superficial reflection may help us manage symptoms temporarily, but deep reflection and healing break the cycle of repeating patterns.

Advanced Strategies for Deep Self-Reflection

⊘ **Journaling:** Go beyond documenting daily events. Use your journal as a tool for in-depth exploration. Write about your emotions, thoughts, and the triggers behind them. Reflect on recurring patterns and themes.

⊘ **Questioning habitual thought patterns:**
  » Challenge your automatic thoughts. Are they based on reality or assumptions?

  » Explore the origins of your beliefs. Are they rooted in past experiences or societal conditioning?

  » Consider alternative perspectives. How else can you interpret the situation?

» Practice mindfulness in order to observe any of your thoughts minus judgment.

✅ **Exploring emotional reactions:**

 Write down the core emotions beneath your reactions (e.g., fear, anger, sadness).

Emotion 1: _____ Emotion 2: _____

Emotion 3: _____ Emotion 4: _____

 Trace these emotions back to their origins in your life. When did you first feel this way?

_____

_____

_____

_____

_____

» Understand the unmet needs or wounds associated with these emotions.

» Develop self-compassion and self-acceptance as you delve into these vulnerable spaces.

Common Barriers to Deep Self-Reflection

✅ **Defense mechanisms:**

Denial: Acknowledge your resistance to facing uncomfortable truths.

Projection: Recognize when you attribute your own feelings to others.

Rationalization: Be honest about when you justify your actions to avoid guilt.

Repression: Uncover hidden memories and emotions gently and gradually.

⊘ **Fear:**

Fear of change: Understand that growth may be uncomfortable, but it leads to greater fulfillment.

Fear of vulnerability: Embrace vulnerability as a path to authentic connection and healing.

Fear of pain: Healing often involves revisiting past wounds, but it's essential for growth.

Deep self-reflection is the key to understanding your authentic self and cultivating emotional resilience. By going beyond the surface and addressing defense mechanisms and fears, you can embark on a journey of profound transformation and true emotional autonomy.

Exercise: The Life Chapters

To help you gain deep insights into your inner self by reflecting on the different chapters of your life.

Life is like a book, with each phase or significant event representing a different chapter that shapes your identity and unconscious patterns. This activity will guide you in exploring these chapters and understanding how they have influenced your present self.

Begin by thinking about the pivotal moments or periods in your life. These could include moving homes, educational milestones, significant relationships, losses, and triumphs. Try to divide your life into distinct chapters based on these events or transitions.

Year	Your Chapter Title - Based on Pivotal Moments and Milestones

 For each chapter you've identified, ask yourself the following questions:

What did you learn about yourself during this period?

_____

_____

_____

_____

_____

Which emotions were most prevalent, and why?

_____

_____

_____

_____

_____

How did your response to challenges evolve?

_____

_____

_____

_____

_____

Explore how each chapter has contributed to your current self. Write down what traits, beliefs, or patterns from the past have persisted and continue to influence your current chapter of life.

_____

_____

_____

_____

_____

Take time to write about each chapter, paying close attention to the emotional undertones and any unacknowledged achievements or regrets. This is the time to let your thoughts and feelings freely flow onto the pages. This exercise aims to bring subconscious patterns to the surface.

_____

_____

_____

_____

_____

Use a journal or notepad to answer the above questions in this exercise for every one of your "Life Chapters."

Once you've completed your journaling for each chapter, take a moment to reflect on how this exercise has offered new perspectives on your behaviors and beliefs.

 Jot down what you have learned about yourself that you hadn't realized before. How can this newfound awareness help you in your journey toward emotional mastery and personal growth?

_____

_____

_____

_____

 ## Exercise: Exploring Painful Events

 Over the course of four consecutive days, allocate time to reflect on a specific event in your life that has been a source of persistent challenge or distress. Dedicate fifteen minutes each day to engage in this exercise. Set yourself a timer so you don't go over.

EVENT:_____

Day One Reflections

_____
_____
_____
_____

Day Two Reflections

_____
_____
_____
_____

Day Three Reflections

_____
_____
_____
_____

Day Four Reflections

_____
_____
_____
_____

Although it might seem simple at first glance, this approach is based on the idea that making small changes can lead to significant and lasting changes in your life. It acknowledges that a lack of clarity or an incomplete personal narrative can often lead to considerable suffering. By the end of four days, you'll likely notice changes in how you perceive the events in your life.

Exercise: Writing in the Third-Person

Now, I encourage you to attempt writing a fully comprehensive account of a distressing or troubling incident but do so from a third-person perspective, using "she," "he," or "it" instead of "I."

Studies have indicated that adopting this approach can yield both immediate and enduring beneficial outcomes (Siegel-Acevedo, 2021). It enables you to attain a fresh viewpoint on the event and create some emotional distance, which may facilitate a smoother process of understanding and healing.

Date: _____,

_____

_____

_____

_____

_____

_____

_____

_____

_____

_____

_____

_____

Advanced Introspection Techniques

 ## *Deep Meditation*

Deep meditation is your portal to the uncharted territories of your subconscious. It's not about clearing your mind but diving into its depths. Here's how to do it (7 Advanced Techniques to Experience Deep Meditation, 2023):

◆ Find a calm, peaceful space free from distractions.

◆ Be in a relaxed position.

◆ Focus on your breath. Breathe slowly and deeply.

◆ As thoughts arise, don't resist them; observe them with curiosity.

◆ Gradually descend deeper into your thoughts, like descending into a well. Explore the layers of your mind.

Remember, this is a practice; the more you meditate, the more profound your insights will become.

Visualization in Shadow Work

Visualization is a potent tool for unearthing the hidden facets of your psyche, particularly in shadow work. Your shadow is the part of you that's often repressed or ignored. To harness the power of visualization in this process, follow these steps:

♦ Find a quiet, comfortable place where you will be calm and uninterrupted.

♦ If you are comfortable doing so, close your eyes and inhale slowly, exhaling slowly, to relax.

♦ Envision yourself entering a room. This room represents your mind, your inner world.

♦ Inside this room, notice various objects. Each object symbolizes a thought, feeling, or memory.

♦ Approach these objects, one by one, and interact with them. Touch them, smell them, really look at them.

♦ Pay attention to the emotions and thoughts that arise as you interact with each object.

> **After the exercise, record your experiences in the space below. Describe how you felt when entering the room and engaging with the objects.**

_____

_____

_____

_____

_____

_____

_____

_____

_____

_____

_____

Advanced Journaling

Journaling is your faithful companion on this journey. This exercise is more than documenting your thoughts and feelings; it's about exploring them. Here's how to take your journaling to an advanced level:

- Allow yourself dedicated time for journaling every day.
- Reflect on significant events or emotions from your day, and delve deep into the underlying causes.
- Challenge your limiting beliefs and thought patterns by asking probing questions.
- Use your journal to track your progress, celebrate your victories, and acknowledge your growth.
- Experiment with various journaling techniques, such as stream-of-consciousness writing, letter writing to your inner self, and future self-journaling.

 ## Dialogue Exercise

Start by selecting an aspect of yourself that you want to explore or understand better. It could be a recurring emotion, a persistent behavior pattern, or a specific belief that you feel is holding you back. This could be anything from your inner critic to your inner child or even a specific emotion like fear, anger, or sadness.

Create a quiet, comfortable space where you can write without distractions. Take a few deep breaths to center yourself and set the intention that you are here to explore and understand this aspect of yourself with compassion and curiosity.

Imagine that you are having a conversation with the chosen aspect of yourself. Start by addressing it directly. For example, if you're dialoguing with your inner critic, you might begin with, "Hello, Inner Critic, I want to understand you better."

Ask open-ended questions to encourage the aspect of speaking freely. You're not looking for quick answers; instead, aim to create a meaningful dialogue.

Here are some examples to get you started:

 As you ask these questions, write down the responses that come to you, even if they seem surprising or contradictory. It's essential to let the aspect speak freely without judgment or censorship. This is a safe space for exploration.

"What is your purpose or role in my life?"

"When did you first appear?"

"What do you need or want from me?"

"How have you been trying to protect or help me?"

_____
_____
_____
_____
_____

"What beliefs do you hold that drive your actions?"

_____
_____
_____
_____
_____

"How have you influenced my choices and decisions?"

_____
_____
_____
_____
_____

Continue the dialogue until you feel that you've reached a natural conclusion. Take some time to think about what you've learned. Summarize the insights, beliefs, or emotions that surfaced during the dialogue.

_____

_____

_____

_____

_____

Now that you have a deeper understanding of this aspect of yourself, consider how you can integrate this newfound wisdom into your life. Are there beliefs or behaviors that you'd like to transform? What steps can you take to align your choices with your desired life trajectory?

_____

_____

_____

_____

_____

 ## *Mindfulness Meditation Practice*

Begin by finding a quiet and comfortable space where you won't be disturbed. Sit or lie down in a relaxed position, ensuring your back is straight but not tense.

Before you start, set an intention for your meditation. What do you hope to gain from this practice today? Is it clarity, insight, or emotional healing? Clarify your purpose.

When you are comfortable, close your eyes and be mindful of your breath. Be mindful of the rhythm of your chest. Anchor yourself to the present moment.

As you breathe in and out, thoughts will inevitably arise. When they do, don't fight them. Instead, acknowledge them without getting involved. Imagine you're sitting on the banks of a river, watching your thoughts flow by.

If a thought triggers a strong emotion, gently label it. For example, "This is a thought about frustration," or "This is a thought about my past." Then, release it, allowing it to drift away like a leaf on a stream.

To deepen your mindfulness practice, start with just five minutes a day. Gradually increase the duration as you become more comfortable. The key is consistency. Here's a suggested progression:

- Week 1: 5 minutes daily
- Week 2: 10 minutes daily
- Week 3: 15 minutes daily
- Week 4: 20 minutes daily

 ### *Exercise: Advanced Shadow Work*

Begin by contemplating a trait or emotion in others that triggers a strong aversion within you. It might be arrogance, impatience, jealousy, or anything that provokes an emotional reaction.

 Ask yourself why this particular trait or emotion bothers you. Write down what it is about this quality that you find repulsive or unsettling. Dive deep into your feelings and thoughts.

_____

_____

_____

_____

Now, consider the possibility that the trait or emotion you dislike in others may reflect an aspect of yourself that you've been neglecting or not wanting to accept. This realization can be challenging, but it is the first step toward growth.

 Write about the trait or emotion you identified, exploring it honestly and without judgment. How might this trait be present within you, even in a subtle or hidden way? Allow your thoughts and feelings to flow freely.

_____

_____

_____

_____

_____

 Dig deeper into your past. Were there any experiences in your childhood or earlier years that might have contributed to the emergence or suppression of this trait within you? For example, have you identified that you dislike anger in others because you have an anger issue yourself? When looking back, can you see a scared inner child who never had control of their surroundings? Are they angry over that loss of control? Reflect on any memories or situations that stand out.

_____

_____

_____

_____

_____

_____

_____

Practice self-compassion as you acknowledge this trait within yourself. Remember that we all have light and shadow within us, and these traits serve as opportunities for growth and transformation.

Contemplate how integrating this trait or emotion can benefit your life. How can understanding and accepting this aspect of yourself lead to emotional autonomy and self-governance?

 Write down what steps you can take to harness this trait's positive aspects and mitigate its negative effects. In the example used above, you may jot down surrounding your inner child in love and protection. Letting them know they don't have to be afraid, allowing them to feel in control now, and acknowledging their anger, allowing them that right to that feeling.

1. _____
2. _____
3. _____
4. _____
5. _____

Commit to specific actions or practices that will help you integrate and transform this trait or emotion positively. These might include meditation, therapy, self-reflection exercises, or simply being more mindful of your reactions and behaviors.

Make it a habit to revisit this exercise periodically to track your progress and ensure that you continue on your path of emotional mastery and personal growth.

Introspection Journaling Prompts

The Core of Identity

This prompt invites you to delve into the layers of your subconscious that influence your self-perception and values. By exploring the origins of your identity, you gain insight into how your past experiences continue to shape your present self.

Engage in deep introspection to explore the roots of your shadow self, delving into early memories, upbringing, and cultural influences. Identify the suppressed or hidden aspects of your personality, acknowledging how societal norms, familial dynamics, and personal experiences shaped them. Reflect on significant life events that may have contributed to forming your shadow self, including traumas or unresolved conflicts. Consider how embracing and integrating these shadow aspects can lead to personal growth and self-awareness.

Purpose and Passion

This prompt encourages you to connect with the deeper layer of your subconscious, helping you uncover passions and purposes that may have been suppressed or overlooked. This gives you the opportunity to align your actions with who you are.

 Focus on exploring any underlying fears, doubts, or insecurities that may be hindering your connection to your true passions and purposes. Examine the ways in which societal expectations, past traumas, or negative self-perceptions have obscured your authentic desires and motivations.

Resistance and Self-Sabotage

Resistance often stems from subconscious beliefs and fears. By examining its roots, you can work to transform these self-sabotaging patterns and move towards emotional autonomy.

 Explore how your subconscious fears and doubts manifest in behaviors that undermine your goals and well-being. What underlying beliefs, past traumas, or insecurities contribute to these patterns?

_____

_____

_____

_____

_____

_____

Emotional Patterns

This prompt guides you to explore the emotional patterns deeply ingrained in your subconscious. Understanding their origins can empower you to consciously respond to situations in ways that align with your desired emotional mastery.

> **Focus on identifying recurring emotions and examining your underlying causes. You should reflect on past experiences, relationships, and childhood influences that may have shaped these patterns.**

_____

_____

_____

_____

_____

_____

Transforming Pain into Wisdom

This exercise encourages you to confront and heal deep-seated wounds in your subconscious. By reframing past pain as a source of growth, you can move towards emotional resilience and self-governance.

Begin by acknowledging the pain or trauma stored in your subconscious, allowing yourself to experience and validate your emotions without judgment fully. Reflect on the lessons and insights that can be gained from these experiences, seeking to understand how they have shaped your beliefs, behaviors, and relationships. Practice forgiveness, both toward yourself and others involved, as you work towards releasing the grip of past wounds.

Heart-Centered Compassion

Place your hand on your heart, gently close your eyes, and visualize someone who embodies boundless loving-kindness, care, and unwavering support for you. This could be a grandparent, whether they are living or have passed away, or even an archetypal or religious figure like Buddha or Jesus. Envision this person or being as someone who wants to care for you, understanding the depths of your heart and soul. Their intention is to protect you. Remember, they love you.

As you feel that love surround you, write a letter to your inner critic. In this letter, tell them exactly what it is you want. What it is you need and how you intend to get there.

Date: _____,

_____

_____

_____

_____

_____

_____

_____

_____

_____

_____

_____

_____

_____

_____

_____

_____

_____

_____

Affirmations for the Subconscious

These affirmations can be even more effective when combined with the introspective exercises and deep subconscious exploration you've undertaken in this workbook. Affirmations, when repeated regularly and sincerely, can create powerful shifts in your subconscious beliefs, paving the way for emotional mastery and lasting resilience. Printable affirmation cards for all the affirmations provided in the book are available at AdvancedShadow.LeighWHart.com, as well as, other helpful resources.

 Here are affirmations that are aligned with the deep subconscious exploration and emotional mastery you're seeking:

- I maintain healthy boundaries, protecting my emotional well-being.
- I observe life's challenges without reacting impulsively.
- I am on a path of healing and have made peace with my past.
- I am in constant connection with my higher self, guiding me wisely.
- I confidently navigate moments of anxiety, knowing I can handle them.
- I articulate my emotions with clarity and authenticity.
- My mind is filled with beautiful, positive memories.
- I am free from self-criticism and hypercritical tendencies.
- Clarity and certainty replace confusion in my life.
- I effortlessly attract what aligns with my authentic self; I don't need to chase.
- I prioritize self-respect over people-pleasing.
- I radiate positive energy, attracting the same into my life.
- I work toward a secure attachment style in all my relationships.
- I release grudges, freeing my heart from negativity.
- I am mindful of my inner power and manifest my desires.
- Forgiveness and letting go come naturally to me.
- I have the freedom to pursue my passions without control, criticism, or comparison.
- I manifest a life filled with positivity and inspiration.
- I fulfill my needs for love and affection through healthy, meaningful connections.
- I maintain a calm, clear, and relaxed state of mind.

We traveled a long way in our exploration through the profound depths of shadow work in this chapter. We visited self-awareness and peeled back the layers of our subconscious to reveal the hidden facets of our psyche. Now, we stand on the threshold of a transformative shift, where self-awareness transitions into the realm of emotional mastery. In the next chapter, we'll dive even deeper, exploring the intricate tapestry of our emotions, understanding their roots, and learning the art of navigating and mastering them. Get ready to embark on a voyage of self-discovery and resilience as we uncover the profound wisdom hidden within the depths of your feelings.

CHAPTER 2
EMOTIONAL MASTERY

Emotional Mastery

> "
> *Your visions will become clear only when you can look into your own heart. Who looks outside, dreams; who looks inside, awakes.* —**Carl Jung**
> "

The purpose of this chapter is to equip you with the skills to navigate through the turbulent waters of emotional intensity. Together, we will delve into the very essence of your emotions, illuminating the pathways that have led you to your current emotional landscape. We will uncover the hidden patterns that have shaped your responses to life's challenges and triumphs, and we will empower you with practical techniques to transform these patterns into sources of resilience and wisdom.

By the end of this chapter, you will emerge with a transformative understanding of your emotions, allowing you to view yourself through a lens of authenticity and acceptance. You will possess the tools needed to navigate emotional intensity with grace.

Understanding Emotional Intensity

Let's begin by diving into the ocean of emotional intensity. Imagine your emotions as waves, some gentle and calming, while others are massive and crash into the shore. This is the essence of emotional intensity—the strength of your feelings, spanning the entire spectrum from the sheer joy that lifts you to the blue skies to the depths of despair that threaten to engulf you.

Think of those moments when your emotions have surged within you, threatening to spill over. It could be the exhilaration of a personal victory or the crushing weight of loss and heartbreak. Emotional intensity is a force that touches every facet of your life. It's not something reserved for special occasions; it's present in your everyday experiences.

Consider a time when you felt an overwhelming passion for a cause or an art form when you sensed the pain of another person so deeply that it became your own, or when your intuition guided you toward the right decision with uncanny precision. These are all manifestations of emotional intensity; you have danced with it more often than you may realize.

Recognizing and naming these intense emotions is a key step on the path to mastery. It's like having a map in an uncharted territory—without realizing the landmarks, you'll remain lost. By understanding emotional intensity, you gain the power to navigate your inner world more effectively.

But how do you know if you are an emotionally intense person? Well, let's take a look at some signs:

◆ **Navigating emotional currents:** Your emotions flow like a wild river, untamed and relentless. You ride the waves of life's highest peaks and venture into the abyss of its deepest lows. The essence of passion courses through your veins, making every moment burst with vividness and vitality.

- **Empathy's deep well:** You've often been labeled an empath because you absorb the emotions of those who share your journey. A profound concern for the pain of others dwells within you, and unethical actions disturb the depths of your being. Your moral compass stands as a guiding beacon in the tumultuous sea of emotions.

- **The art of perceptive insight:** Your intuition is your superpower, a finely tuned instrument that effortlessly discerns diverse energies, patterns, and connections in your surroundings. Bright lights and sudden sounds may catch you off guard, a testament to your heightened awareness.

- **Journeying through the inner cosmos:** Your imagination knows no boundaries. Books, music, and art serve as sustenance for your soul, and the enigmatic allure of the spiritual realm beckons you. Your insatiable curiosity and intellectual fervor propel your quest for meaning and personal growth.

- **Unleashing creative potential and wrestling with existential questions:** You possess an unyielding drive to unravel life's purpose, an insatiable hunger to ascend higher. You're a tireless innovator and visionary, but this pursuit occasionally leads you to confront profound existential quandaries that can stir turbulent emotions.

Emotionally intense people make up a significant portion of our population, roughly 15-20% (Roselle, 2018). Yet, despite your unique gifts and experiences, you often feel misunderstood. Many of us will struggle to label and harness our deep emotions effectively.

Your emotional intensity is characterized by heightened and intense feelings, a constant stream of positive and negative emotions that can sometimes blend into a whirlwind. At times, these emotions may become so overwhelming that they feel uncontrollable, clouding your ability to think clearly and leaving you feeling lost.

I want you to know that you have the power to channel this intensity into a force for healing, growth, and transformation. Let's try some exercises to do just that.

Exercise: Emotional Exploration Scale

This tool will empower you to gain a profound awareness of your emotional states, from the mildest hints to the most intense surges. It's a key step toward responding to your emotions with intention and mastery instead of impulsively.

Gaining insight into the nature of an emotion and how it evolves in intensity is a fundamental initial stride toward mastering emotional control.

 ### *Creating Your Emotion Exploration Scale*

Select an emotion you wish to delve into and explain its progression from the gentlest manifestation at level 1 to its most intense expression at level 10.

Emotion You Want to Explore: _____

♦ **Thoughts:** Begin with the lowest possible level (1) of this emotion. What are the thoughts that accompany it? How do they manifest in your mind?

♦ **Behaviors:** Progress to level 2. How do your behaviors change as this emotion intensifies? What actions or reactions do you notice?

♦ **Symptoms / Physical Sensations:** Move on to level 3. Be mindful of the physical sensations associated with this emotion. What do you feel in your body? Any tension, aches, or other sensations?

Continue this process all the way up to level 10, noting the thoughts, behaviors, and physical sensations at each level of intensity for the chosen emotion.

Level	Thoughts	Behaviors	Symptoms & Sensations
1			
2			
3			
4			
5			
6			
7			
8			
9			
10			

Using Your Emotion Exploration Scale

Now that you have your scale, use it as a daily journaling tool for a week. Throughout the day, reflect on your emotional states and rate them on this scale. Here's how it can empower you:

◆ **Awareness:** You become acutely aware of their nuances by actively observing and rating your emotions. You can identify the subtle shifts from mild to intense, gaining insight into your emotional landscape.

◆ **Control:** Understanding how your thoughts, behaviors, and physical sensations change as an emotion intensifies gives you the power to take charge. It's like knowing the terrain before you embark on a journey.

◆ **Response vs. reaction:** Armed with this awareness, you can respond to your emotions with intention. Instead of reacting impulsively, you can choose how you want to navigate the emotional landscape.

This exercise is a profound step in your journey toward healing and growth. It's about gaining mastery over your emotions and creating a life that aligns with the happiness and fulfillment you deserve.

Techniques for Handling Emotional Intensity

 ## *Integrating Mindfulness and Shadow Work*

Imagine the synergy of two profound approaches, mindfulness and shadow work, coming together to illuminate your path. Mindfulness, as defined by Jon Kabat-Zinn, is about paying purposeful, nonjudgmental attention to the present moment (J, 2023). Shadow work is an embodied exploration of your inner world. Together, they empower you to take charge of your healing journey.

In shadow work, we often ask, "What needs to happen between these two conflicting aspects of yourself in order for you to have what you want?" This question invites you to become the architect of your own transformation. Similarly, in mindfulness, we inquire, "What do you feel in your body right now? Can you describe it as a sensation? Now, can you fully experience that sensation just as it is without turning away from it?" These questions empower you to guide your healing process, recognizing that you hold the wisdom and authority over your journey.

Combining shadow work and mindfulness allows you to make peace with the aspects of yourself you've been at war with. It's a journey of self-liberation, where you confront and honor all parts of your being, even the ones you've pushed into the shadows. Remember, a liberated person is one who is willing to meet every facet of themselves with compassion and understanding.

Now, let's explore an advanced exercise to seamlessly integrate mindfulness with your shadow work, paving the way for deep healing and lasting transformation.

Exercise: Exploring Your Emotional Roots

Answer these questions using this scenario: You often find yourself in toxic relationships, repeating the same patterns.

Write down the recurring patterns you've noticed in your relationships.

_____
_____
_____
_____
_____

Now, reflect on your childhood experiences and family dynamics. How might they have contributed to these patterns?

_____
_____
_____
_____
_____

Dive into your memories and feelings. What emotions are attached to these patterns?

_____
_____

Answer these questions using this scenario: You struggle with self-doubt and negative self-talk.

List the most common self-doubting thoughts that haunt you.

_____

_____

_____

_____

_____

Challenge these thoughts by asking yourself: What events from my past might have planted these seeds of doubt?

_____

_____

_____

_____

_____

Jot down the emotions associated with these thoughts.

_____

_____

You need to be consistent in doing these exercises. This will help you unlock your emotions, understand yourself, and continue to heal.

 ## Exercise: The Release Breath

Imagine a scenario where you've uncovered a deep-seated belief that has been sabotaging your relationships. This belief stems from a childhood experience buried in your subconscious. It's causing emotional pain, and you're determined to release it.

Close your eyes, take a few moments, and truly focus on your breath. Take a deep breath through your nose, letting your lungs fill completely. Feel the sensation of this happening.

As you exhale through your mouth, visualize the belief you want to release. See it as a dark cloud or heavy weight leaving your body with each breath out.

Continue this cycle, inhaling positivity and healing, exhaling the belief that no longer serves you.

As you progress, you might feel emotions surfacing. Allow them to flow without judgment, knowing this process is essential for healing.

Repeat this exercise daily, gradually observing how the emotional pain diminishes, making room for transformation and growth.

Exercise: The Inner Sanctuary Breath

In moments of heightened emotional turmoil, it's important to have a safe space within yourself. This exercise helps you create that inner sanctuary.

Close your eyes and take a few calming breaths.

Visualize a serene, safe, and beautiful place within your mind—a place where you feel completely at peace. This could be a beach, a forest, a bookstore, or even your bedroom.

Imagine yourself walking into this sanctuary. Feel the peace, security, and unconditional love that it offers.

As you breathe deeply in this inner sanctuary, allow any emotional pain to surface. Acknowledge it without judgment.

With each breath in this sacred space, envision healing light filling your entire being, soothing the emotional pain.

When you're ready, return to your physical surroundings, carrying the peace and healing from your inner sanctuary with you.

Practice this exercise whenever you need to find emotional refuge and nurture your inner strength.

Exercise: Cognitive Reframing for Transformation

Now that you've explored the roots of your feelings and emotions, it's time to reframe your beliefs and thoughts. Remember, change begins with awareness.

 Answer these questions using this scenario: You have a fear of failure that holds you back from pursuing your dream job.

Write down the negative beliefs related to this fear. For example, "Why bother? I know I am not smart enough."

Negative Belief #1: _____

Negative Belief #2: _____

Negative Belief #3: _____

Counter each belief with a positive, empowering affirmation. For example, "I am well educated and worthy of this promotion."

Positive Affirmation for Negative Belief #1:

_____
_____
_____
_____

Positive Affirmation for Negative Belief #2:

_____
_____
_____
_____

Positive Affirmation for Negative Belief #3:

Repeat these affirmations daily, and continue to record your progress below for one week.

Days	Daily Progress from Affirmations
Monday	
Tuesday	
Wednesday	
Thursday	
Friday	
Saturday	
Sunday	

Journal Prompts: Emotional Mastery in Depth

Use these journal prompts to identify
EMOTIONAL TRIGGERS:

List the situations or circumstances that consistently trigger your most challenging emotions.

_____

_____

_____

_____

_____

Reflect on the underlying beliefs or experiences that might fuel these triggers. Can you think of how they might be relevant to your current life?

_____

_____

_____

_____

_____

_____

Use these journal prompts to explore UNHELPFUL COPING MECHANISMS:

Recall instances when you turned to unhelpful coping mechanisms (e.g., avoidance, excessive use of substances, etc.) to deal with intense emotions. What emotions were you trying to escape or numb?

_____

_____

_____

What were the consequences of these coping mechanisms on your long-term well-being and relationships?

_____

_____

_____

_____

_____

 Use these journal prompts to explore
TRANSFORMATIVE COPING STRATEGIES:

Share examples of positive coping strategies you've experimented with to manage intense emotions effectively.

_____
_____
_____
_____
_____
_____

Discuss the impact of these strategies on your overall emotional well-being. Take a moment and reflect on what changes you have noticed in your life.

_____
_____
_____
_____
_____
_____
_____

Use these journal prompts to work on HEALING YOUR INNER CHILD:

Connect with your inner child by visualizing a moment from your childhood when you felt vulnerable or hurt. Ask yourself what your inner child needs to hear from you specifically at this time.

_____
_____
_____
_____
_____
_____
_____

Reflect on how providing love and reassurance to your inner child can positively impact your current emotional experiences.

_____
_____
_____
_____
_____
_____
_____

Exploring Advanced Self-Acceptance

Have you ever asked yourself if you truly accept who you are?

It might seem like an unusual question, for isn't self-acceptance something we naturally do as we navigate our daily lives?

Yet, the reality is that self-acceptance isn't always our default state. Many of us find it challenging to embrace ourselves fully. While it's relatively easy to acknowledge our positive attributes, what about our flaws and failures? Should we accept those too?

In truth, that's precisely what we should strive for. Self-acceptance, as the name suggests, is the state of wholeheartedly embracing oneself. Authentic self-acceptance means accepting who you are without any conditions, qualifications, or exceptions. This definition underscores the importance of embracing every aspect of yourself. It's not sufficient to only celebrate the good, the valuable, and the positive in yourself. To attain genuine self-acceptance, you must also welcome the less desirable, the negative, and even the aspects you consider ugly or "bad" within yourself.

Accepting the very things we yearn to change about ourselves is hard, so we need to be kind to ourselves while doing so. However, paradoxically, it's through genuine self-acceptance that the transformative journey toward self-improvement truly begins. To embark on the path of self-growth, we need not just self-acceptance but unconditional self-acceptance.

You acknowledge that you've made mistakes and possess imperfections, yet you refuse to let them define you. Practicing unconditional self-acceptance empowers you to not only love yourself but also to embrace your genuine self, enabling you to work on improving the traits and qualities you find less desirable.

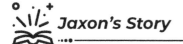

Jaxon's Story

In this case study, we meet Jaxon, a talented artist with a passion for creativity and a history of self-doubt stemming from his experiences as a freelancer. Despite holding a senior position in a stable company, he still grapples with self-doubt that limits his pursuit of new opportunities. Jaxon sought coaching to overcome these challenges and regain confidence in his abilities.

During our sessions, we focused on aligning his head, heart, and body centers of intelligence to ensure he was fully committed to taking action. In our first session, we emphasized the importance of understanding his current reality and identifying the barriers preventing him from moving forward.

As Jaxon began to open up, he shared the emotional weight of his past struggles and fears of failure and judgment. Through thoughtful questioning, we challenged his negative thought patterns and encouraged him to view his fears from different angles. This process helped him realize that many of his fears were fragile and didn't hold up to a reality check. He also recognized that he had evolved and possessed the power to create a better life using his skills and talents. This revelation brought a sense of liberation and newfound energy to move forward.

In subsequent sessions, we delved deeper into exploring Jaxon's goals, creating execution plans, and allowing room for adjustments. We also explored methods to help him overcome recurring self-doubt by using metaphors and self-reflective questions like "Is this true?" and "How does this thinking serve me at this moment?"

A valuable lesson emerged when Jaxon initially overcommitted himself due to his enthusiasm, leading to burnout. We adjusted his plan to include more consideration for rest and recharge, leading to smoother progress.

In the final session, we reviewed the progress against his initial goals and found that the majority had been achieved with ongoing support structures in place. Jaxon's self-doubt had transformed into self-acceptance and confidence, and he had developed a toolkit to address self-doubt whenever it resurfaced.

 ## Exercise: *Mapping Emotional Landscapes*

Creating an emotions map uses non-verbal expression to learn to identify emotions and develop self-awareness.

Take a deep breath and center yourself in the present moment.

 In the space below, start drawing your emotional map. You can use symbols, shapes, and colors like rivers or mountains to represent different aspects of your inner world.

Think of the map as a landscape, with regions symbolizing different feelings. For instance, a mountain might represent anger, a calm lake could signify peace, and a river might depict sadness.

Now, label each area on your map with the emotions you feel most strongly. Use different colors or symbols to denote the intensity of these emotions.

Create paths, bridges, or roads on your map to represent how you transition from one emotion to another. This will help you understand the interconnectedness of your feelings.

Take your time with this exercise. There's no need to rush. Allow your emotions to flow onto the paper as you create your unique emotional landscape.

As you complete this exercise, remember that your emotional map is a reflection of your inner reality. It's okay if it feels complex or messy; that's perfectly normal. This map is the first step towards gaining clarity about your emotions and how they shape your experiences.

 ## Exercise: Self-Acceptance Letter

In this exercise, we'll explore the profound practice of self-acceptance. This is a powerful tool that will help you embrace your emotions, past experiences, and your authentic self without judgment. Let's get started:

 Begin your letter by addressing yourself. Use your own name, and express your intention to accept and understand your emotions without any criticism or judgment. For example:

"I am writing this letter to you with an open heart and a sincere desire for self-acceptance. Today, I commit to embracing all of my emotions without judgment."

1 Now, reflect on past situations where you may have been critical of your emotional responses. Think about moments when you wished you had reacted differently or when you felt guilty or ashamed of your feelings. Add these situations to your letter, but do so with empathy and understanding. For instance:

"I remember that time when [describe the situation]. In the past, I've been critical of myself for feeling [describe your emotion]. I now realize that it was a valid emotional response to the circumstances I was facing."

2 Extend forgiveness to yourself for any self-criticism or judgment you've held. Understand that you were doing the best you could with the tools and knowledge you had at the time. For example:

"I forgive myself for any harsh judgments I've made about my emotions in the past. I recognize that I was learning and growing, and I am ready to release any self-blame."

3 Affirm your right to feel all your emotions. Remind yourself that every emotion you experience is a natural part of being human. You are allowed to feel joy, sadness, anger, fear, and everything in between. Write empowering statements like:

"I have the inherent right to feel all of my emotions, no matter how uncomfortable or challenging they may be. My emotions are valid, and they are essential to my personal growth."

4 Conclude your letter by making a commitment to treat yourself with compassion moving forward. Pledge to continue this journey of self-acceptance and integrate these insights into a healthier and more accepting self-view. For example:

"I commit to treating myself with the same kindness and understanding that I would offer to anyone I love and respect. I embrace self-acceptance as an ongoing practice and promise to nurture my emotional well-being."

Dear _____,   Date: _____,

_____

_____

_____

_____

_____

_____

_____

_____

_____

_____

_____

_____

_____

_____

_____

_____

Love, _____

After you've written your letter, take some time to read it aloud to yourself. Feel the emotions and intentions behind your words. This exercise may bring up feelings and insights— embrace them with an open heart.

As you move forward, keep this letter handy. Revisit it whenever you find yourself struggling with self-criticism or judgment. Use it as a reminder of your commitment to self-acceptance and the journey towards emotional mastery and healing.

Journal Prompts: Acceptance in Depth

Start by defining what self-acceptance means to you personally. What does it look like? How does it feel? Write down your own unique understanding of self-acceptance.

_____
_____
_____
_____
_____

List the barriers you've faced in fully accepting yourself. Be honest and specific. It could be past traumas, societal pressures, or negative self-talk. Write them down without judgment.

_____
_____
_____
_____
_____

Identify someone you admire for their self-acceptance and self-love. What qualities or practices do they possess that you could learn from? How can you incorporate these into your life?

_____

_____

_____

_____

_____

Envision yourself in the future, fully embracing self-acceptance. What does this version of you look like, act like, and feel like? How does this vision inspire and motivate you?

_____

_____

_____

_____

_____

Affirmations for Self-Acceptance

⊘ ***I embrace my flaws and imperfections; they make me unique.*** *Your imperfections are what make you beautifully human. Embrace them as part of your individuality and strength.*

⊘ ***I release the need for perfection and embrace my journey of growth.*** *Understand that growth is a process, and it's okay to make mistakes along the way. Each step is a part of your beautiful journey.*

⊘ ***I forgive myself for past mistakes and use them as stepping stones to a better future.*** *Acknowledge that we all make mistakes, but it's what we learn from them that matters. Forgive yourself and let go of any self-blame.*

⊘ ***I acknowledge my emotions, and they do not define me.*** *Recognize that while your emotions are valid, they do not define your entire being. Your power lies within how you choose to react to them.*

⊘ ***I release the need for external validation; I validate myself.*** *Seek validation from within rather than relying on others to affirm your worth. You are your own greatest source of validation.*

⊘ ***I deserve love, respect, and kindness, both from myself and others.*** *Set high standards and boundaries for how you should be treated, and don't settle for less.*

Embrace change and personal growth as natural processes of life. Every transformation brings you closer to your true self.

Remember, affirmations are not just words but powerful tools for shifting your mindset and beliefs. Use them daily, write them down in your journal, and repeat them with intention.

As we conclude this chapter on the mastery of emotions, take a moment to acknowledge the tremendous progress you've made in understanding and accepting your emotional self. Now, as we turn our attention to the next chapter, I invite you to discover the profound influence of past experiences, particularly trauma, on the intricate patterns of your emotions. Brace yourself for a voyage of self-discovery as you navigate the depths of your past to illuminate the path toward true and lasting healing.

CHAPTER 3
ECHOES OF THE PAST

Echoes of the Past

> **"**
>
> *Although the world is full of suffering, it is also full of the overcoming of it. –Helen Keller*
>
> **"**

I want to welcome you to chapter three. Take a breath and realize how far you've come. You've already taken courageous steps on the path to self-awareness and personal transformation. You've begun to peel back the layers of your psyche, uncovering the shadows that have quietly shaped your life. Now, you're ready to dive even deeper, to confront the echoes of your past that continue to reverberate in your present.

In this chapter, we will embark on a journey that will show the profound impact trauma can have on our shadows. Trauma, whether it's from childhood experiences, past relationships, or unexpected life events, can cast long shadows over our lives, influencing our thoughts, emotions, and behaviors in ways we might not even be aware of. It's time to shine a light on those shadows, to understand how they've been woven into the fabric of your existence.

We'll also explore the critical role of the ego in protection. Your ego, like a vigilant guardian, may have developed coping mechanisms to shield you from the pain of your past. However, these well-intentioned defenses can sometimes hinder your growth and healing. We'll learn how to work in harmony with the ego, gently coaxing it to loosen its grip on the past and embrace the potential for a brighter future.

But fear not, for this chapter is not just about uncovering wounds; it's about healing them. I'll provide you with a toolkit of advanced techniques that will empower you to confront and release the emotional burdens of your past. These techniques are not mere Band-Aids or temporary fixes; they are profound methods for true healing and transformation.

By the time you reach the end of this chapter, you'll have a deeper understanding of your trauma, a newfound ability to accept and work through it, and the practical skills needed to embark on a journey toward lasting healing. You'll be equipped to rewrite the script of your life, breaking free from cycles that no longer serve you and stepping into the life you deserve.

The echoes of the past are waiting to be heard, understood, and ultimately set free.

Understanding Trauma

Trauma is an intricate and deeply personal experience, and it's vital to comprehend that it's not the event itself but your individual experience of it that defines its impact. Trauma can manifest in various forms, and its effects ripple through both your physical and psychological realms.

Trauma leaves imprints on your body and mind. Physically, it can sensitize your stress response system, leading to heightened levels of stress hormones like cortisol. While these hormones serve a crucial role in dealing with immediate threats, chronic exposure can lead to adverse health conditions.

Furthermore, trauma's indirect effects can manifest in unhealthy coping mechanisms, such as smoking or drinking, which provide temporary relief but prolong emotional pain.

Different Forms of Trauma

Trauma knows no boundaries and can manifest in various settings. Here are some forms of trauma (Types of Trauma, 2023):

- **Type 1 trauma:** Also known as "big T trauma," this refers to single-incident traumas that occur unexpectedly. It includes events like severe illness or injury, violent assault, sexual assault, traumatic loss, and witnessing acts of violence or terrorism.

- **Type 2 trauma:** These traumas are experienced over a prolonged period and often involve interpersonal relationships. Examples include sibling abuse, childhood emotional abuse, domestic violence, and emotional neglect.

- **Historical, collective, or intergenerational trauma:** These traumas affect entire communities or groups, leaving emotional and psychological scars. Examples include the Holocaust, racism, slavery, and forced displacement.

◆ **Vicarious or secondary trauma:** This type occurs when you listen to someone else's traumatic experiences and can result in you experiencing similar symptoms as the person who went through the trauma.

◆ **Little (t) trauma:** These are everyday experiences that may not seem traumatic on the surface but can be emotionally significant, such as moving to a new house or losing a job.

It's essential to recognize that trauma is pervasive. In the United States alone, an estimated 90 percent of adults have experienced a traumatic event at least once in their lives. Additionally, approximately 7-8% of all adults will develop post-traumatic stress disorder (PTSD) during their lifetime (Khoddam, 2021).

Initial Reactions to Trauma

When you encounter trauma, your body and mind react in various ways. Initial reactions may include exhaustion, confusion, sadness, anxiety, agitation, numbness, dissociation, and physiological arousal. It's normal to experience a combination of these symptoms.

Trauma sensitizes the body's stress response system, making it more reactive to stress and increasing the release of cortisol, the primary stress hormone. While cortisol is crucial in certain situations, chronic elevation can lead to health issues like depression and heart disease (Khoddam, 2021).

Moreover, trauma's psychological effects often surface first, disrupting your daily life with symptoms like depression, anxiety, anger, intense fear, flashbacks, and paranoia. These experiences can alter your perceptions, making you feel that the world is unsafe and others are dangerous.

 ## *Exercise: Identifying Trauma*

In this exercise, we will guide you through the process of assessing your past experiences to determine if they might qualify as trauma. Recognizing trauma is a crucial step toward healing and growth.

Before you begin, put yourself in a calm, serene space. Take a few deep breaths to calm your mind and create a sense of presence.

 Begin by reflecting on various life experiences. These can include events from your childhood, adolescence, and adulthood. Write down any experiences that come to mind, whether positive or negative. Beside each of the experiences you write down, answer the questions listed.

Repeat this exercise for as many experiences that you want to uncover.

Experience: _____

_____

_____

_____

_____

Questions: Y   N

Did this experience involve a threat to your life or   ○   ○
physical safety?

Did you experience intense fear, helplessness, or   ○   ○
horror during or after this event?

Did this experience have a lasting impact on your   ○   ○
mental or emotional well-being?

Did it disrupt your sense of safety or trust in others?   ○   ○

Has this experience continued to affect your   ○   ○
thoughts, emotions, or behaviors in a significant
way?

Experience: _____

_____

_____

_____

_____

Questions: Y   N

Did this experience involve a threat to your life or   ○   ○
physical safety?

Did you experience intense fear, helplessness, or   ○   ○
horror during or after this event?

Did this experience have a lasting impact on your   ○   ○
mental or emotional well-being?

Did it disrupt your sense of safety or trust in others?   ○   ○

Has this experience continued to affect your   ○   ○
thoughts, emotions, or behaviors in a significant
way?

Use your journal or notepad to repeat this exercise for additional experiences. Or go to AdvancedShadow.LeighWHart.com to print out additional pages for this exercise.

Review your answers to the questions for each experience. If you answered "yes" to one or more of these questions, it suggests that the experience may have the qualities of trauma.

 After assessing all the experiences, rank them in terms of the level of emotional impact they had on you. Use a scale from 1 to 10, with 1 being the least impactful and 10 being the most impactful.

Take a moment to reflect on any patterns or commonalities among the experiences you've identified as potential trauma. **Are there recurring themes or types of events that stand out?**

This exercise is a valuable tool for assessing whether certain experiences in your life may qualify as trauma. Remember that trauma is a complex and individualized experience, and this self-assessment is just the first step in understanding and addressing it. Your feelings and experiences are valid, and seeking support when needed is a sign of strength and self-care. In the subsequent sections of this workbook, we will explore advanced methods to heal and grow beyond trauma.

How Trauma Effects the Shadow

When trauma strikes, it can be so overwhelming that we struggle to cope with the emotional chaos it unleashes. Often, we lack the emotional capacity, understanding, or support to deal with it in a healthy way at that moment. Consequently, what we cannot process and integrate during the traumatic  event becomes locked down and concealed in our shadow.

The shadow, as you know from your previous work, is the repository of all that we repress, deny, or hide about ourselves—emotionally, physically, and psychologically. Trauma, being an intense and painful experience, is often too much to bear, so we bury it in the shadows, creating unconscious behavior and belief patterns. These patterns serve as a protective mechanism, shielding us from the pain and allowing us to maintain a semblance of safety.

However, here's the paradox: These hidden traumas continue to influence our lives and relationships, seeking resolution and yearning to be acknowledged and integrated. When you find yourself triggered emotionally, it's often the surface-level reaction of these unresolved traumas, concealed deep in your shadow, clamoring for your attention. Yet, we develop intricate and unconscious mechanisms to ignore, suppress, or avoid these triggers, which perpetuate the unhealthy cycles of behavior.

Moreover, your nervous system intervenes, sounding an alarm, insisting it's not safe to approach these painful emotions. This is when fear and resistance take over, pushing you into a fight, flight, or freeze reaction.

But here's the silver lining: these challenging emotions residing in your shadow—such as grief, sadness, rage, hopelessness, envy, and more—are actually guiding lights. They offer you a path forward, but the emotions are often too overwhelming to confront, so they remain as unconscious reactions.

This disconnection from emotional intelligence has a profound impact on how you communicate with yourself and others. It can give rise to mental health conditions, deeper imbalances within your psyche, soul, and body, and enable unhealthy, fractured, and toxic relationships to persist. The effects of trauma intertwine, creating a tapestry that alters your identity, personality, and character, affecting how you relate and interact with others.

Forming and maintaining healthy relationships can become a challenge as internal conflicts around love, trust, communication, commitment, and intimacy emerge. This can lead to social isolation and difficulties with social cues and norms.

The ripple effect of trauma doesn't stop with you; it extends to your family, your community, and even your workplace. Unresolved trauma can lead to relationship conflicts, stress, and strain in your interactions with others and can significantly impact your performance and ability to lead effectively.

Remember, we carry the experiences of our spiritual and bloodline ancestors within us. Their traumas, whether individual or collective, are imprinted in our psyche and cellular memory. Unresolved trauma tends to find its way into our lives and shapes our self-perception and relationships.

Through generations, unconscious patterns are passed down, reflected in our beliefs and behaviors within the modern context. This can disrupt your quest for a unique identity, love, safety, security, stability, and emotional connection.

You might find yourself drawn to toxic and unhealthy relationships, mirroring the unresolved trauma passed down through generations, which may make you believe you deserve no better. Emotions, too, can be passed from parent to child, carrying forward through familial lines, seeking expression and integration.

Exercise: Writing Your Trauma Narrative

Approach this exercise at your own pace, and don't rush through it. If at any point it feels too overwhelming, take a break and return to it when you feel ready. Remember, you are in control of this process.

Begin by selecting one particular traumatic event from your past that you believe may have contributed to your current shadow aspects. It's essential to focus on one event at a time to ensure you can explore it thoroughly.

Create an outline for your narrative, breaking it down into the following sections:

◆ **Setting:** Describe where and when the event occurred.

_____

_____

_____

_____

_____

◆ **Facts:** Provide a detailed, objective account of the event. Stick to the facts without embellishment or judgment.

_____

_____

_____

_____

_____

◆ **Feelings:** Reflect on the emotions you experienced during and after the event. How did it make you feel? Be honest and raw in expressing your emotions.

_____

_____

_____

_____

_____

◆ **Senses:** Explore the sensory details associated with the event. What did you see, hear, smell, taste, and touch during that time?

See: _____

Hear: _____

Smell: _____

Taste: _____

Touch: _____

 Now, using your outline as a guide, write your trauma narrative. Write in the first person, as if you're reliving the experience. Feel free to use as much detail as necessary to capture the event and your emotional response fully.

After you've completed your narrative, take some time to reflect on what you've written. Pay attention to any insights or realizations that emerge. Are there patterns or recurring themes in your narrative that relate to your current shadow aspects? How has this event shaped your beliefs and behaviors?

_____

_____

_____

_____

_____

_____

_____

As you reflect, practice self-compassion. Remember that the emotions you experienced during the traumatic event were valid reactions to a challenging situation. Be kind to yourself as you explore these feelings.

This exercise is a powerful step toward healing. Once you've gained insights into how your past trauma may have shaped your shadow aspects, you can begin the process of cognitive reframing and creating new, healthy habits that align with the life you deserve.

Writing your trauma narrative is a brave and important step in your journey of self-discovery and healing. It may be emotionally challenging, but remember that you are on the path to understanding and transforming your shadow aspects. This exercise is a valuable tool to help you break free from cycles that no longer serve you and create a brighter future.

The Ego as the Protector

Let's start by introducing the concept of the ego and understanding its pivotal role in your life. Your ego is not your enemy; it's your guardian, your protector. It's the part of you that has developed over time to shield you from psychological pain, especially the pain experienced by your inner child. This is an essential aspect of our exploration because it helps us to see the ego not as an obstacle but as a powerful ally in our healing journey.

Trauma, as you may recall, comes in various forms, both big "T" and small "t." Trauma isn't limited to extreme experiences; it can also stem from seemingly smaller yet significant events in our lives. These experiences shape our perceptions and emotions, often leading to the development of our ego as a protective mechanism. It's essential to recognize that the ego's intentions are rooted in the desire to keep you safe.

You might wonder why, when you've attempted to heal old wounds, you've sometimes found yourself feeling worse. This paradoxical experience is not uncommon. The ego acts as the gatekeeper to these deep-seated wounds, and it needs to grant permission for access. When we rush into healing without acknowledging the ego's role, it perceives danger and tries to shut down the process, resulting in symptomatic upheaval.

So, how do we move forward? We do it by respecting the gatekeeper, by recognizing that there is an ego tirelessly trying to protect your most vulnerable wounded parts. Building a good relationship with your ego is the key to making the healing process smoother. When you approach your ego with genuine understanding and compassion, it can learn to trust you, gradually stepping aside to allow access to those buried wounds.

Embracing your ego offers more than just a smoother healing journey; it can transform the way you navigate life. As you recognize what your ego is trying to do for you, it will not only step aside more often but also evolve into something far more helpful and effective. The internal conflict will diminish, replaced by harmony and understanding.

It's crucial to dispel the myth of the loving shadow self that rejects humanity. This idea often leads to shadow bypassing, where we ignore or suppress our true feelings. The reward of a healthy relationship with your ego is that you bring all your feelings out of the shadows for healing. No emotion is deemed unworthy of your care once you understand the ego's role in protecting you.

 ## *Ego Exercise*

This exercise is designed to help you understand how your ego has acted as a protector during times of stress and challenge. By recognizing these instances, you can gain invaluable insights into the roots of your emotions and begin the process of healing and transformation.

> **Take a few deep breaths to center yourself and prepare for introspection.**
>
> **Think back to moments in your life when you've faced significant stress, challenges, or emotional turmoil.**

Write down any instances from your childhood, adolescence, or adulthood where you faced stress and turmoil. Remember, this is a safe space for reflection, so take your time and be gentle with yourself.

_____

_____

_____

_____

_____

Now, focus on how your ego responded during those challenging times. Your ego often acts as a protector, employing defense mechanisms to shield you from emotional pain or discomfort. Write down specific instances where you can recognize your ego's protective actions. For example:

◆ Did your ego create a facade or mask to hide your true feelings from others?

◆ Did it engage in self-sabotaging behaviors as a way to maintain control?

◆ Did it push people away to avoid vulnerability?

◆ Did it resort to blaming others or external circumstances to avoid taking responsibility?

_____

_____

_____

_____

_____

Next, explore the underlying intentions or beliefs that drove your ego's protective actions. What was it trying to achieve? Was it trying to protect your self-esteem, prevent rejection, or maintain a sense of control? Write down your insights.

_____

_____

_____

_____

_____

Consider the long-term consequences of your ego's protective actions. Did they ultimately serve your best interests, or did they create more pain and limitations in your life? Jot down how these actions may have contributed to the cycles you wish to break.

_____

_____

_____

_____

_____

Jot down anything you took away from this exercise. Acknowledge the protective role your ego played during challenging times, and express gratitude for its attempts to shield you. However, also recognize that some of these protective mechanisms may no longer serve your growth and healing.

_____

_____

_____

_____

_____

Finally, set your intentions for moving forward. What advanced methods can you employ to address and heal these deep-seated wounds? How can you reframe your cognitive patterns and create healthier habits aligned with the life you truly deserve? Write down concrete steps you plan to take to break free from the cycles that have held you back.

Step 1: _____

Step 2: _____

Step 3: _____

Step 4: _____

Step 5: _____

Healing the Inner Child

Childhood trauma, whether it was overt abuse or subtle neglect, can leave lasting imprints on your inner child. These experiences, often buried deep in your subconscious, can persist into adulthood, shaping your relationships, self-esteem, and overall well-being.

Imagine your inner child as a young version of yourself, still carrying the wounds and fears from your past. These unhealed wounds can manifest in various ways, such as:

♦ **Repeating patterns:** You might find yourself stuck in destructive patterns of behavior, continually attracting the same types of people or situations that mirror your past experiences.

♦ **Low self-esteem:** Childhood trauma can erode your self-worth, making it challenging to establish healthy boundaries or prioritize your needs.

♦ **Emotional reactivity:** You might react to present-day situations with disproportionate emotions as if you were reliving past traumas.

♦ **Avoidance:** Some individuals distance themselves from their emotions or situations that trigger painful memories, preventing true healing and growth.

The first step in healing your inner child is acknowledgment and acceptance. It's about recognizing that the emotions and behaviors you experience as an adult often have roots in your childhood experiences.

Exercise: Connecting With Your Inner Child

This exercise is designed to create a heartfelt connection with your inner child and begin the process of healing. By writing a letter to your inner child, you can express love, understanding, and support, which can be incredibly therapeutic.

Take a few deep breaths to calm your mind. Close your eyes and imagine yourself in a peaceful, safe, and nurturing place. Visualize a protective cocoon of light surrounding you.

Begin to imagine your younger self, the version of you who experienced pain, trauma, or challenging emotions during childhood. Picture this child clearly in your mind. It can be helpful to keep a physical picture of you as a child close by.

Address your inner child directly. You can begin with "Dear [Your Name]'s Inner Child" or choose any form of address that feels comfortable to you.

In your letter, express your love, compassion, and understanding toward your inner child. Let them know you are here to listen, support, and nurture them.

Recognize the pain and struggles your inner child experienced. You can mention specific memories or emotions that you know affected them deeply.

If you feel that your adult self played a role in neglecting or mistreating your inner child, offer a heartfelt apology. Forgive yourself for any past actions or inactions that contributed to their pain.

Promise your inner child that they are safe now and that you will protect and care for them. This assurance can help rebuild trust.

Invite your inner child to communicate with you. Ask them if there's anything they want to share, express, or ask for. Encourage them to speak freely.

Express your commitment to healing and nurturing your inner child. Sign the letter with love and care.

Take a moment to read the letter aloud if you feel comfortable doing so. This strengthens your connection to your inner child. You can also keep this letter in a safe place to revisit as needed.

Guided Meditation Exercise: Nurturing Your Inner Child

- Sit or lie down in a relaxed position, close your eyes, and take a few deep, cleansing breaths. Let go of any tension or stress you may be carrying, and allow yourself to become fully present in this moment.

- Now, imagine yourself in your happy place. This will be different for each of you.

- As you stand in this peaceful place, you notice a small, innocent child nearby. This child represents your inner self, the part of you that has been hurt and wounded in the past. Approach the child gently, with love and compassion in your heart.

- Imagine yourself kneeling down in front of this inner child, making eye contact, and offering a warm, loving smile. Extend your hand to them, inviting them to come closer. As they approach, you can see the pain and vulnerability in their eyes.

- Begin to speak to this inner child. Let them know that you are here to offer them love, support, and understanding. Tell them that you are sorry for any pain they have experienced and that you are committed to healing and nurturing them.

- This is the time to actually ask your inner child what they need from you. Listen attentively to their words or feelings that arise within you. Your inner child may express fears, hurts, or desires that have been long buried. Embrace these emotions with empathy and without judgment.

◆ Now, imagine yourself wrapping your inner child in a warm, protective embrace. Feel the love and compassion flowing from your heart to theirs. Assure them that you are here for them and you will always be there to provide the comfort and support they need.

◆ Take a few moments to sit with your inner child, letting them feel your presence and love. Allow any emotions to surface, and offer comfort as needed.

◆ As you continue to nurture your inner child, remind them that you are now an adult who can protect and guide them through life's challenges. Promise them that you will work together to heal old wounds and create a happier, healthier future.

◆ Open your eyes and take a deep breath, knowing you've taken a significant step in your healing journey.

If you would like to explore working more on your inner child, I want to direct you to the second book in my series, *Reparenting Your Wounded Inner Child*," for more information on this subject and a book full of additional guided exercises.

Reparenting Yourself

Reparenting yourself is like becoming the loving and caring parent you needed but didn't have during your childhood. It's a process of self-nurturing and self-compassion that allows you to heal deep-seated wounds, address unresolved issues, and reprogram your subconscious mind for emotional mastery.

Practical steps for self-reparenting (Walsh, 2023):

◆ **Identify needs that haven't been met:** Begin by recognizing the unmet emotional needs from your childhood. Reflect on what you wished for as a child, such as safety, love, validation, or understanding.

- **Self-compassion:** Treat yourself with love, kindness, and understanding. Know that you are worthy of love, care, and acceptance, just as you are. Practice positive self-talk and challenge the inner critic.

- **Set boundaries:** Establishing healthy boundaries is essential for self-reparenting. Learn to say "no" when necessary and protect your emotional well-being. Boundaries are the framework for self-respect and self-care.

- **Self-care rituals:** Develop a consistent self-care routine that nourishes your body, mind, and spirit. This can include meditation, journaling, exercise, creative outlets, or spending time in nature. Find what brings you joy and relaxation.

- **Inner child work:** Connect with your inner child through visualization or meditation. Imagine yourself as a vulnerable, young version of yourself and offer comfort, validation, and love. Revisit your past hurts and let your inner child know they are safe now.

- **Reframe negative beliefs:** Challenge the negative beliefs and thought patterns stemming from your childhood experiences. Replace them with affirmations that reinforce your self-worth and potential.

- **Consistency and patience:** Be patient with yourself and stay committed to your journey. Reparenting takes time, but every step you take is a step closer to the life you deserve.

Remember, you have the power to rewrite your story and create a future free from your past's limitations. By embracing the process of self-reparenting, you are nurturing your inner child and providing the love and care that was missing. This advanced step in your shadow work will pave the way for emotional mastery, cognitive reframing, and a life filled with love, authenticity, and growth.

Exercise: Self-Parenting Plan

Part 1: Identifying Your Ideal Parent

 Take some time to think about your upbringing. Consider both the positive and negative aspects of your relationship with your parents or caregivers.

What were the qualities or actions of your parents that you found comforting, nurturing, and supportive? Jot down any positive traits or behaviors that stand out.

_____

_____

_____

_____

_____

Reflect on your current needs, both emotional and practical. What do you believe your ideal parent should provide or have provided in terms of emotional support, guidance, love, and care? List these needs and desires.

_____

_____

_____

_____

_____

Now, compile a list of qualities and characteristics you envision in your ideal parent. This could include traits like empathy, patience, understanding, or the ability to provide emotional validation. Imagine the perfect parent who can meet your current needs.

_____

_____

_____

_____

_____

_____

_____

_____

Part 2: Designing Your Self-Reparenting Plan

 Review your list of qualities of the ideal parent and the needs you've identified. Highlight the qualities you believe you already possess or the ones you can cultivate within yourself.

Based on the qualities you've highlighted, jot down specific self-nurturing goals for yourself. For instance, if you value empathy, a goal could be to practice self-empathy regularly. If you need patience, a goal might be to develop patience through mindfulness practices.

_____

_____

_____

_____

_____

_____

_____

Break down each goal into actionable steps. Write down what concrete actions you can take to embody these qualities and meet your own needs. Be specific and realistic. For example, if your goal is to be more understanding of yourself, one action step could be to journal about your thoughts and feelings daily.

Action Step #1: _____

Action Step #2: _____

Action Step #3: _____

Action Step #4: _____

Action Step #5: _____

Consider sharing your self-reparenting plan with a trusted friend who can provide support and hold you accountable for your progress.

Remember that self-reparenting is an ongoing process. Be open to adapting and evolving your plan as you discover new aspects of your needs and qualities you wish to develop.

 ## *Journal Prompts for Trauma and Growth*

How has your trauma affected your life up to this point? Consider your relationships, self-esteem, and overall well-being. What patterns or beliefs have emerged as a result of your experience?

_____

_____

_____

_____

_____

Reflect on how your perception of your trauma has evolved over time. Have there been any pivotal moments or realizations that changed the way you view it? How has this affected your healing journey?

_____
_____
_____
_____
_____

Recall instances in your life when you displayed incredible resilience or strength despite the trauma you've experienced. How can you draw on these moments to empower your healing journey?

_____
_____
_____
_____
_____

Reflect on the concept of forgiveness—both forgiving yourself and, if applicable, forgiving those who may have caused your trauma. What might forgiveness mean to you, and how can it support your healing process?

_____
_____
_____
_____
_____

Take a moment to acknowledge and celebrate the growth you've already achieved. Write down the positive changes you've seen in yourself as a result of your commitment to healing.

_____
_____
_____
_____
_____
_____
_____

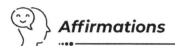

Affirmations

Here are some affirmations to empower and support you:

- ◆ I am resilient, and I have the inner strength to face my deepest wounds.

- ◆ I embrace the discomfort of healing, knowing that it leads to growth and transformation.

- ◆ I am the architect of my emotional well-being, shaping a brighter future.

- ◆ I release the hold of past pain, allowing space for new healing and growth.

- ◆ I am worthy of joy, love, and abundance.

- ◆ I trust my inner wisdom to guide me on this healing journey.

- ◆ I have the power to rewrite my story, free from the constraints of the past.

- ◆ I am capable of breaking free from old patterns and creating new, healthy habits.

- ◆ I lovingly acknowledge and heal the wounds that have held me back.

- ◆ I deserve happiness, and I'm committed to doing the inner work to achieve it.

Choose which affirmations resonate with you the most and recite them daily.

As we conclude this chapter on healing trauma and its profound influence on our shadow selves, we've unveiled the complex interplay between our past wounds, the protective role of the ego, and the nurturing of our inner child. Now, as we transition into the next chapter, we will explore practical techniques that empower us to conquer the negative thoughts and self-doubt that have lingered as echoes of our past trauma. Building upon the healing work we've undertaken, these techniques will guide us to greater self-compassion, self-awareness, and resilience.

CHAPTER 4
THE CHATTER OF
THE MIND

The Chatter of the Mind

> 66
>
> *A man is but the product of his thoughts. What he thinks, he becomes. –Mahatma Gandhi*
>
> 99

Here in Chapter 4, we dive headfirst into the core of your being, focusing on one of the most pivotal aspects of your inner landscape: your thought patterns. This chapter is a journey that requires courage, patience, and a deep desire for change, and you've already proven yourself more than capable of rising to the challenge.

The thoughts that occupy your mind shape your reality. They influence your emotions, actions, and, ultimately, the life you lead. But it's not just about positive thinking or quick fixes; it's about understanding the root of your thought patterns, addressing their origins, and creating lasting change from within.

Unmasking Negative Thought Patterns

Do you ever feel like you're your own harshest critic? Are you familiar with the experience of being overwhelmed by a constant stream of negative thoughts, regardless of how positive your circumstances may appear?

Perhaps you frequently find yourself caught up in a cycle of worrying about hypothetical scenarios or becoming anxious over potential negative outcomes, even when there's no tangible reason for such anxiety.

How does the concept of negative thinking relate to our exploration of the shadow self? Have you ever found yourself pondering the question, "Am I fundamentally a flawed person?" Perhaps you recall a specific incident where you said or did something completely out of character, leaving you at a loss for an explanation. Maybe this action harmed someone else, or perhaps it inflicted harm upon you. It's possible that you felt a deep-seated fear upon witnessing this unfamiliar aspect of yourself.

Before you could even begin to unravel the complexity of the situation, you were confronted with a profound question: Are you, at your core, a bad person? How did you react to this question? Did you hastily dismiss it, afraid of what the answer might reveal? Alternatively, did this inquiry send you spiraling into negative thought patterns?

The following are common negative thought patterns (Marteka, 2019):

◆ **All-or-nothing thinking:** This is the tendency to see things in extreme black-and-white terms, with no middle ground. It's the belief that if you're not perfect, you must be a failure.

◆ **Overgeneralization:** Here, you take a single negative event and generalize it to a pattern of defeat in your life. One setback becomes a belief that "everything always goes wrong."

◆ **Mental filter:** This involves focusing solely on the negatives while ignoring any positives. It's as if you're wearing a mental filter that screens out all the good things.

◆ **Discounting the positive:** You tend to undermine or dismiss positive experiences or compliments, thinking they don't count or are unimportant.

◆ **Magnification/minimization:** This distortion involves blowing your mistakes out of proportion (magnification) while minimizing your successes or strengths.

◆ **Emotional reasoning:** The deep-seated belief that your feelings are facts. If you feel it, it must be true, even if there's no evidence to support it.

◆ **"Should" statements:** You impose unrealistic expectations on yourself, using words like "should," "must," or "ought to." This often leads to guilt and self-criticism.

◆ **Labeling:** You label yourself or others based on mistakes or shortcomings, reducing complex human beings to a single negative trait.

◆ **Personalization and blame:** You take on responsibility for events that are beyond your control or blame others for your own feelings and problems.

Exercise: Identifying Your Personal Negative Thought Patterns

I would like you to spend some time reflecting on your thoughts and feelings. Here's a simple exercise to help you identify your unique negative thought patterns.

 For one week, whenever you notice a negative thought, write it down. Include the date, the situation that triggered the thought, and the emotions you felt.

Date	Situation/Trigger	Emotions	

After the week, review your entries. Are there recurring themes or thought patterns? Pay attention to keywords or phrases that pop up frequently.

_____

_____

_____

_____

_____

Try to connect these negative thought patterns with aspects of your shadow self. Are there unresolved issues, past traumas, or suppressed emotions that seem related to these thoughts?

_____

_____

_____

_____

_____

Challenge each identified negative thought pattern. Ask yourself if it's based on reality and if not, reframe it into a more balanced and constructive thought.

_____

_____

_____

_____

_____

Exercise: Unmasking the Origins of Negative Thoughts

This exercise will guide you in uncovering the root causes of your recurring negative thoughts, shedding light on your shadow aspects that may be influencing your emotions and behaviors.

◆ **Prepare your space:** Find a quiet and comfortable space where you won't be interrupted. Take a few deep breaths to center yourself and create a sense of inner calm.

List your frequent negative thoughts: Make a list of the negative thoughts that often cross your mind. These can be self-critical thoughts, doubts, fears, or any recurring negative patterns you've noticed. Be very specific. For example:

"I'm not worthy."

"I'm a failure, and I am constantly messing up."

Negative Thought #1: _____

_____

Negative Thought #2: _____

_____

Negative Thought #3: _____

_____

Negative Thought #4: _____

_____

Negative Thought #5: _____

_____

Reflect on the origin: For each negative thought on your list, take some time to explore its possible origins. Write down any memories, events, or experiences from your past that might have contributed to the formation of this thought pattern. Be honest with yourself, and don't shy away from uncomfortable memories or emotions. For example:

"I remember being criticized by my parents for my grades when I was a child."

Origin for Negative Thought #1: _____

_____

Origin for Negative Thought #2: _____

_____

Origin for Negative Thought #3: _____

_____

Origin for Negative Thought #4: _____

_____

Origin for Negative Thought #5: _____

_____

Emotional exploration: Now, next to each negative thought and its possible origin, describe the emotions you associate with them. How do these thoughts make you feel? Are there any physical sensations that accompany these emotions? Write down your emotional responses honestly. For example:

"The thought 'I'm not good enough' makes me feel anxious and inferior. My chest tightens when I think about it."

Emotion for Negative Thought #1: _____

Emotion for Negative Thought #2:_____

Emotion for Negative Thought #3:_____

Emotion for Negative Thought #4:_____

Emotion for Negative Thought #5:_____

Identify patterns: After completing this exercise for all the negative thoughts on your list, take a step back and look for commonalities or recurring themes in your origins and emotional responses. Are there any patterns or connections you notice?

_____

_____

_____

_____

_____

Strategies for Positive Change

In this section, we'll explore strategies for positive change, offering you practical techniques to shift from negative to positive thought patterns. Remember, this work may be challenging, but the rewards are immense.

 ## *Strategy 1: Shadow Archetype Exploration*

We all possess a myriad of archetypal energies within us. These archetypes represent different facets of our psyche, and understanding them can be a powerful tool for personal growth. By delving into the shadows, you can begin to unravel the root of your feelings and emotions.

 Identify and explore the <u>SHADOW ARCHETYPES</u> within (Aletheia, 2023):

The addict: Recognize when you become compulsive or overly attached to something, whether it's a substance, behavior, or even a person. Write down what you are trying to escape or numb with this addiction.

_____

_____

_____

_____

The beggar: Explore moments when you feel unworthy, as though you're constantly seeking validation or handouts. Write down what you believe the fear or scarcity driving this mindset is.

_____

_____

_____

_____

The fanatic: Notice when you become obsessive or extreme in your beliefs or actions. Jot down what you think could be deeper insecurities or fears you are masking with this fanaticism.

_____

_____

_____

_____

The judge: Reflect on instances when you find yourself overly critical, not just of others but also of yourself. Write down what unresolved judgments or self-doubts lie beneath this harshness.

_____

_____

_____

_____

The martyr: Pay attention to times when you sacrifice your own needs excessively for others. What unmet needs or guilt underlie this self-sacrifice? Write them down.

_____

_____

_____

_____

The saboteur: Examine moments when you self-sabotage your own success or happiness. Jot down what fears or limiting beliefs are holding you back from achieving your potential.

_____

_____

_____

_____

The victim: Identify situations where you feel powerless or constantly victimized. What unresolved traumas or patterns of victimhood are you carrying? Write them down.

_____

_____

_____

_____

 Alternatively, you may choose to work with the INNER CHILD ARCHETYPES, which can provide a different perspective on your subconscious patterns (Edwards, 2021):

The caretaker: When do you feel the need to take care of others at the expense of yourself? What childhood experiences might have led to this role?

_____

_____

_____

_____

The overachiever: Explore the moments when you push yourself excessively. What childhood expectations or pressures have contributed to this need for constant achievement?

_____

_____

_____

_____

The underachiever: Reflect on times when you hold yourself back from success. What past failures or criticisms might be fueling this fear of failure?

_____

_____

_____

_____

The rescuer/protector: Notice when you feel compelled to rescue or protect others. What unresolved needs for safety or validation are you seeking through this role?

_____

_____

_____

_____

The life of the party: Examine situations where you feel the need to be the center of attention. What childhood experiences might have led to this desire for approval?

_____

_____

_____

_____

The yes-person: When do you find it hard to say no, even when it's against your best interests? What fears of rejection or conflict are driving this behavior?

The hero-worshipper: Pay attention to moments when you put others on a pedestal. What unmet needs for guidance or role models are you seeking to fulfill?

Recognizing Influence and Reflection: Once you've identified these archetypes within yourself, take time to reflect on how they influence your daily life and decision-making. Are they protectors, trying to shield you from perceived threats or disruptors, holding you back from your true potential?

 Strategy 2: Emotional Alchemy Practice

Let's begin by understanding the essence of emotional alchemy. It's not just about managing or suppressing your emotions; it's about transforming them into fuel for your growth and healing. It's about taking the negative energy tied to your shadow aspects and transmuting it into a positive force that propels you forward.

■ Step 1: Identifying the Root Emotion

To practice emotional alchemy effectively, you must first become a detective of your own emotional landscape. The shadows often manifest as complex emotions that are deeply intertwined. Begin by identifying the core emotion that fuels your shadow aspect. This will require journaling and deep introspection.

Start by answering the following questions.

What emotion lies at the heart of your shadow aspect?

Can you label it as shame, anger, fear, or something else entirely? If so, write about what you feel it may be.

Emotion: _____

_____

_____

_____

Be patient and compassionate with yourself during this process, as it can be challenging to pinpoint the root emotion.

■ Step 2: Consciously Transforming Emotions

Once you've identified the core emotion, it's time to embark on the transformative journey. Remember, you're not trying to erase these emotions; you're converting their energy into something constructive.

◆ **Breathing techniques:** Deep, mindful breathing can be an incredibly powerful tool. When you feel the intense emotion associated with your shadow rising within you, pause and take slow, deliberate breaths. As you inhale, imagine drawing in calm and healing energy; as you exhale, release the negative emotion. This simple practice can help you regain control over your emotional responses.

♦ **Visualization:** Visualization is a potent method for emotional alchemy. Close your eyes and picture the challenging emotion as a tangible object or substance. Then, imagine transforming it into something positive. For instance, if you're dealing with anger, visualize it turning into a fiery passion for positive change. If it's fear, imagine it becoming a wellspring of courage.

▊ Step 3: Embracing Perspective Shifts

As you practice emotional alchemy, you'll start to notice a profound shift in your perspective. What once seemed like insurmountable obstacles now become opportunities for growth and empowerment. Remember that healing and growth often occur in the discomfort zone. Embrace the process as an essential part of your journey to a more fulfilling life.

By transforming your emotions, you'll not only gain control over your reactions but also tap into a wellspring of inner strength and resilience. These newfound emotional tools will become the foundation upon which you build the life you deserve.

 ### *Strategy 3: Shadow Role-Play Exercise*

In Strategy 3, we will delve into the powerful practice of shadow role-play, which will help you understand and integrate your shadow aspects in a safe and controlled way.

Before we dive into the exercise itself, let's briefly revisit why this strategy is so essential. Our shadow aspects are those parts of ourselves that we often repress, deny, or hide from the world. They are rooted in our past experiences, conditioning, and unresolved traumas. These shadows can take control in certain situations, causing us to react in ways that are not aligned with our true selves.

By engaging in shadow role-play, you can bring these hidden aspects to light, examine them from a different perspective, and consciously alter their influence on your life. This practice allows you to gain insights into the root causes of your emotions and behaviors, paving the way for profound healing and personal growth.

How To Shadow Role-Play:

◆ Find a quiet, comfortable place where you won't be disturbed. Set the intention that this is a safe and judgment-free space for self-exploration. You might want to light a candle or play soothing music to enhance the atmosphere.

◆ Imagine stepping into the shoes of your shadow self. Visualize yourself fully embodying the traits, beliefs, and emotions associated with this aspect. Feel what it's like to be this version of yourself.

◆ Now, think about situations in your life where your shadow aspect tends to take control. It could be moments of anger, fear, self-doubt, or any other challenging emotion. Choose one scenario to focus on.

◆ Act out the scenario as if you were your shadow self. Let yourself feel the emotions and react as you usually would. This may bring up discomfort, but remember, this is a safe space for exploration.

◆ After you've played out the scenario, pause and take a deep breath. Now, rewind the situation in your mind and consciously alter the outcome.

I want you to write down how your ideal self would respond in this situation. How can you shift your reactions to align with your true values and intentions?

_____

_____

_____

_____

_____

 Reflection: Write down your observations and insights from this role-play exercise. What did you learn about your shadow self? How did it feel to change your reactions consciously? What new possibilities emerged for handling similar situations in your daily life?

_____

_____

_____

_____

_____

Integration into Daily Life

The true power of shadow role-play lies in its ability to help you transform your daily interactions and responses. To reinforce this practice:

♦ Regularly engage in shadow role-play sessions for different scenarios.

- Challenge yourself to embody your shadow aspect in progressively difficult situations.

- Gradually integrate your newfound awareness and conscious responses into your daily life, one step at a time.

 Strategy 4: Creative Expression

Creative expression is a remarkable way to connect with your subconscious mind. It offers a medium through which your shadow self can communicate, often revealing emotions, memories, and thoughts that may be difficult to access through traditional introspection. This strategy encourages you to step out of your comfort zone, allowing your shadow to express itself in a tangible form.

Exercises in Creative Expression

- **Painting your emotions:** Take out some art supplies and let your emotions guide your brushstrokes. Don't worry about creating a masterpiece; focus on the emotions flowing through you. Use colors, shapes, and patterns to represent what's hidden in your shadow. When you're finished, take a step back and observe what you've created. What emotions or insights does it evoke?

- **Music as a mirror:** If you play an instrument or enjoy creating music, use it as a tool for self-expression. Compose a piece of music that reflects the emotions you're struggling with. Let the melodies and rhythms mirror your inner world. Play it back to yourself and listen attentively, allowing the music to speak to you.

- **Words unleashed:** Writing is a powerful way to connect with your shadow self. Try writing in a journal, but this time, let your shadow take the pen. Allow it to write freely, without censorship or judgment. Let it express its fears, regrets, and desires. Read what you've written with curiosity and compassion.

♦ **Adult coloring:** Adult coloring can be a surprisingly effective tool for shadow work and bringing out aspects of our shadow self. While it might seem like a simple and enjoyable activity, the process of coloring can tap into our subconscious. It allows for emotional release, creative freedom, and mindfulness while you focus on your art. I have added some coloring sheets for you to experiment with at the end of this section.

Once you've completed a creative expression exercise, it's time to dive into interpretation:

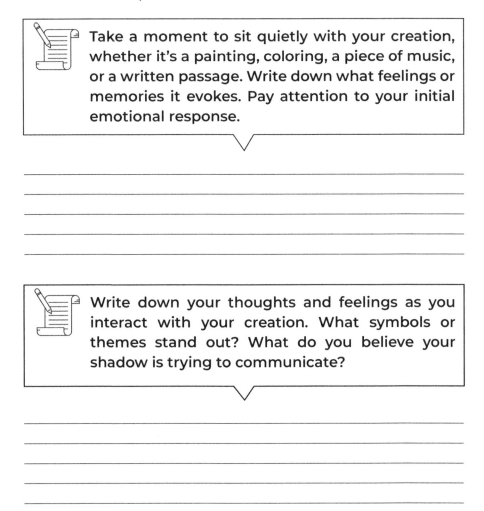

Take a moment to sit quietly with your creation, whether it's a painting, coloring, a piece of music, or a written passage. Write down what feelings or memories it evokes. Pay attention to your initial emotional response.

Write down your thoughts and feelings as you interact with your creation. What symbols or themes stand out? What do you believe your shadow is trying to communicate?

The Healing Power of Acceptance

Creative expression provides a safe and non-judgmental space for your shadow self to reveal its truths. Remember that the goal of this strategy is not just to uncover hidden messages but also to foster understanding and acceptance.

As you engage in these exercises, you may start to notice shifts in your perception and emotional landscape. Embrace these changes with an open heart, and be patient with yourself. Healing takes time, and each step you take brings you closer to the life you deserve.

Patterns and Triggers: The Path to Liberation

It's time to explore the intricate relationship between negative thought patterns and emotional triggers, offering you practical methods for identifying and transforming these triggers into conscious responses.

 ## *How Do We Know We're Triggered or Experiencing Emotional Triggers?*

Emotional triggers often operate beneath the surface of our conscious awareness. They can be sneaky, slipping into our thoughts and reactions before we even realize it. To gain mastery over them, we must first become adept at recognizing their presence.

Start by paying attention to your bodily sensations. When you're triggered, your body often sends unmistakable signals, such as:

◆ sweating

◆ racing heart

◆ chest pain

◆ nausea

◆ shaking

◆ tightening in your stomach or chest

◆ being overly hot

◆ lump in your throat

◆ sense of numbness or dissociation

These physical cues are your body's way of alerting you to a potential trigger. Don't ignore them; they are valuable messengers.

Next, observe what arises in your mind when you experience these bodily sensations. Emotional triggers are often accompanied by intense feelings, such as:

◆ panic

◆ rage

◆ fear

◆ grief

◆ disgust

◆ anger

These feelings can send your nervous system into a state of "fight, flight, freeze, or fawn." Depending on your learned coping mechanisms, you may respond with behaviors like yelling, crying, shutting down, or even being aggressive.

But here's the key: the more adept you become at noticing these bodily sensations and intense feelings, the more control you gain over your reactions. You create a vital space between your emotions and your responses, allowing you to consciously recognize that you're triggered and that you have alternatives to your usual reactions.

This is the turning point where you can engage your "processing emotional triggers" plan, whatever that may be. It's a moment for inner inquiry and reaching out to your support systems and resources to help you confront, experience, address, and process the emotions that are surfacing.

Identifying Emotional Triggers

Let's illustrate this with an example. Imagine a person named Erin. When she experiences emotional triggers, she often reacts without realizing it, expressing her feelings through angry outbursts and hurtful words directed at her partner. During these moments, she may use harsh language, bring up past mistakes, highlight her partner's flaws, and eventually find herself in tears, seeking forgiveness.

Erin's lack of awareness regarding her emotional triggers perpetuates emotional distress for both herself and her relationship. This underscores the significance of recognizing emotional triggers. Without this self-awareness, individuals can find themselves in a state of "reaction autopilot," where their responses are primarily dictated by their emotions. However, by consciously identifying these triggers, one gains the ability to shift into a more rational and emotionally healthy response mode.

Self-awareness is your ally at every step of this journey. As you delve deeper into your psyche, you gain more control over your life. I want to bring Jean-Paul Sartre's words into the picture here, "Freedom is what you do with what's been done to you (Oppong, 2023)." This journey is about taking charge of your healing and growth.

5-Step Process for Integrating Emotional Triggers or Healing Shadows

 Now, let's dive into a 5-step process that will help you integrate emotional triggers and heal your shadows. This process is where journaling and worksheets become your valuable companions.

▮ Step 1: Notice & Name

Imagine yourself as an "emotion hunter" living in the present moment, constantly aware. When you feel intense emotions or emotional triggers, notice and name them. Is it anger? Sadness? Hurt? If you can't pinpoint the emotion, acknowledge that you're feeling something and jot it down. This step sets the stage for mindful meditation in the present moment.

Date	Intense Emotion or Emotional Trigger

Step 2: Pause & Witness

Once you've identified the emotion, pause before reacting. Take deep breaths, in for a count of 4 and out for a count of 6. Shift your awareness to your heart area and become a witness to your emotions. Instead of saying, "I am angry," say, "I see you, Anger. I feel you right now." By doing this, you separate yourself from the emotion, allowing your empowered self to take control.

Step 3: Explore What Happened and What's Going On In The Body

Take a moment to explore the situation that triggered your emotions. Jot down the details: was it a person, a situation, a place, or a noise? Keep in mind that these external factors often serve as triggers to draw your attention to underlying emotions and shadows. Then, turn your focus inward and examine what's happening in your body. Is your heart racing? Is your stomach tight? Are you clenching your teeth? This step is all about "feeling to heal" as you defuse, heal, and integrate old wounds.

Details:

_____

_____

_____

_____

What's happening in your body?

_____

_____

_____

_____

Step 4: Reflect

Delve deeper into your past to find connections. Think back to a time when you felt a similar way as a child or in the recent past. Act as a detective, conducting inner inquiries. Recognize that these strong emotions are opportunities for healing something from your past, not for retraumatizing yourself. If you've been doing inner child work, ask your inner child what they'd like to show you. If you've been working on shadow integration, inquire about what the shadow wants. Write down your findings and shower love on your inner child or shadow side.

_____

_____

_____

_____

_____

Step 5: Process & Integrate

Identify any core wounds that might be seeking recognition and healing. Write them down, offering words of understanding and compassion. This is a mindful meditation in the emotional present moments of life. By acknowledging these wounds, you thaw out the frozen trauma imprints, allowing for their processing and release. This is how you become triggered less and respond more proportionally and healthily to life's challenges.

_____

_____

_____

_____

_____

What Story Is Playing?

When triggered, an old story often plays in your mind—a story that no longer serves you. Notice the thoughts or belief patterns associated with your triggers. Write to increase self-awareness, not to judge yourself. Recognize extreme thoughts or beliefs that are simply untrue. Core wounds are common, and everyone has them to some degree. The key is to become aware of them and to heal them.

Sometimes, triggers are linked to feeling out of control. Recognize these triggers and engage techniques like breathwork and visualization to address the intense bodily emotions (often anxiety) that arise. Understand that not everyone is a threat, and you can regain a sense of safety and control through self-awareness.

Unmet core needs can also trigger strong emotions. Do you know your core needs for feeling safe, loved, autonomous, peaceful, respected, valued, and secure? Make connections between your triggers and unmet needs. Learn to communicate your needs instead of reacting or shutting down.

Exercise: Pattern Interrupt Technique

The pattern interrupt technique is a powerful and advanced method designed to interrupt and alter your automatic, reactive patterns when triggered by challenging emotions or situations. It helps you regain control over your responses, allowing you to replace old, unhealthy habits with new, empowering ones (Mindfulness STOP Skill, 2023).

- **S =** Stop everything the moment you become aware that you're feeling charged up. This will create some space between you and the situation.

- **T =** Take a deep breath, and bring yourself into a state where you can refrain from reacting.

- **O =** Objectively observe what is happening in the moment and how you are feeling. Give yourself a few moments to pull back your energy so that you can become conscious of your thoughts, words, and actions prior to moving forward.

- **P =** Proceed cautiously and consciously in a way that will unfold potential rather than perpetuate any drama.

Facing the Inner Critic

The inner critic, that relentless voice inside your head, often acts as your harshest judge and critic. It can sow seeds of doubt, self-criticism, and even self-sabotage. This inner monologue is not your true voice; it's a collection of internalized external influences and societal expectations that have taken root within you over the years.

Your inner critic can be sneaky, disguising itself as self-preservation or wisdom. But in reality, it often holds you back from your full potential and keeps you trapped in cycles of self-doubt and negativity.

Identifying the Inner Critic

To begin your journey of facing and taming your inner critic, it's crucial first to identify its presence in your life. Here are some prompts and exercises to help you recognize when your inner critic is active.

Take a moment to sit quietly and pay attention to your thoughts. Can you distinguish between the voice of your inner critic and your authentic self? The inner critic often sounds harsh, judgmental, and critical, while your true self is compassionate and understanding.

Recording Your Inner Critic

Whenever you notice your inner critic surfacing, jot down the thoughts and feelings it generates. Be specific and include the context of the situation.

_____

_____

_____

_____

_____

Triggers and Patterns

Reflect on situations or events that tend to trigger your inner critic. Is it more active during moments of stress, when facing criticism from others, or when you're stepping out of your comfort zone? Recognizing these patterns will help you anticipate and address the inner critic's appearance.

_____

_____

_____

_____

_____

Externalized Voices

Consider whose voices you may have internalized over the years. Were there parents, teachers, friends, or authority figures whose expectations and criticisms you've absorbed as your own? Recognizing these external influences can be an important step in disentangling them from your true self.

Impact on Decision-Making

Think back to significant decisions or choices you've made in your life. How did your inner critic influence those decisions? Did it lead you to play it safe, avoid risks, or hold back from pursuing your passions?

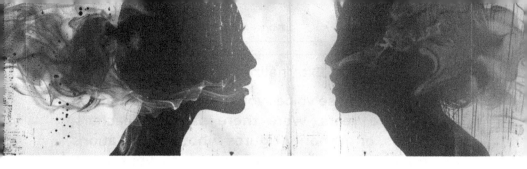

Inner Critic Exercise

 Your inner critic might be loud and unrelenting at times, but you have the strength to transform its messages into tools for positive change.

◆ **Invoking your inner critic:**

» Close your eyes and imagine your inner critic as a separate entity or character. Give it a name or visualize it as a person, object, or even an animal. This will help you externalize it and create a distinct presence.

◆ **Begin the dialogue:**

» Write down a conversation between yourself and your inner critic. Start by addressing it by its name or form. For example, "Hello, Inner Critic. I know you're here to protect me, but I'd like to understand you better."

_____
_____
_____
_____
_____

◆ **Ask questions**:

» Inquire about its motives. Why does it say the things it does? What is it trying to protect you from? What past experiences or beliefs influence its messages? Allow your inner critic to express itself fully.

◆ **Listen actively:**

» After asking a question, pause and imagine what your inner critic might say in response. Write down its answers without judgment. Let it speak freely.

◆ **Challenge its messages:**

» Once you've heard what your inner critic has to say, respond to its messages. Use your newfound awareness to question the validity of its claims. Challenge its negative beliefs with more compassionate and rational thoughts.

◆ **Find common ground:**

» Look for common ground or shared values between you and your inner critic. Often, it's trying to protect you or prevent you from experiencing pain. Acknowledge its intentions and express gratitude for its concern.

◆ **Reassess and reframe:**

» With this understanding, work together with your inner critic to reframe its messages in a more constructive way. Transform its critical voice into a supportive and encouraging one.

- ◆ **Set healing intentions:**

  - » Write down your intentions for healing and personal growth. What new, healthy habits do you want to cultivate? How can you use the insights gained from this dialogue to align with the life you deserve?

  _____

  _____

  _____

  _____

  _____

- ◆ **Closing the dialogue:**

  - » Thank your inner critic for its input, and assure it that you'll be more aware of its presence moving forward. Close the conversation with a sense of empowerment and self-compassion.

 Affirmations to Counteract Your Inner Critic

I have included a list of affirmations that can help counteract the messages of the inner critic. Be mindful to choose the affirmations that resonate most with you on a personal level. These affirmations will be your allies in moments of self-doubt, helping you reprogram your subconscious mind for healing and growth:

⊘ "I release the need for perfection; I am enough as I am."

⊘ "I am in control of my thoughts, and I choose positivity and self-compassion."

⊘ "I trust in my ability to handle any challenges that come my way."

⊘ "I deserve abundance and success in all areas of my life."

⊘ "I am resilient, and I have proven that I bounce back from setbacks stronger than before."

⊘ "I let go of the need for approval from others; I approve of myself."

⊘ "I am a magnet for positive experiences and people who uplift me."

 ### *Building a Bridge Over Self-Doubt*

Self-doubt often lurks in the shadows of our subconscious, and it's essential to bring it into the light of your conscious awareness. Your journey begins with acknowledging and embracing your shadow self—the parts of you that you may have suppressed or denied over the years.

- **Increased self-awareness:** The first step in conquering self-doubt is to become intimately familiar with the hidden aspects of your psyche. This increased self-awareness is the cornerstone of personal growth. By exploring your shadow self, you'll uncover the origins of your self-doubt, which may be rooted in childhood experiences, past traumas, or societal conditioning.

- **Improved self-confidence:** As you delve deeper into your shadow self, you'll start to understand the underlying beliefs and thought patterns that fuel your self-doubt. With this newfound awareness, you can begin the process of reprogramming your mind for improved self-confidence.

You'll learn to challenge those negative beliefs and replace them with empowering ones.

◆ **Relief from negative emotions:** Self-doubt often leads to a plethora of negative emotions such as anxiety, fear, and insecurity. By shining a light on your shadow self, you can unravel the emotional knots that have been holding you back. This release of negative emotions will pave the way for a more serene and harmonious inner landscape.

◆ **Increased empathy:** Exploring your shadow self isn't just about confronting your own darkness; it also fosters increased empathy and compassion toward others. As you come to terms with your own imperfections, you'll become more accepting and understanding of the imperfections in others.

◆ **Healing past hurts:** Many of our self-doubts are born from past wounds. By exploring your shadow self, you can address these deep-seated wounds and begin the process of healing.

 Exercise: Cognitive Reframing

 Step 1: Identify the Self-Doubt

Begin by finding a quiet, comfortable space where you can reflect without distractions. Now, think about a specific self-doubt that has been lingering in your mind. It might be a belief like "I'm not good enough," "I'm always a failure," or "I'll never succeed." Write down this self-doubt in your journal as clearly and honestly as possible.

Self Doubt: _____

_____

_____

_____

_____

Step 2: Examine the Evidence

Now, let's challenge this self-doubt with rationality and self-compassion. Ask yourself: What evidence do you have that supports this self-doubt? Be as objective as possible. Write down any instances or experiences that seem to validate this belief.

_____

_____

_____

_____

_____

Step 3: Explore Alternative Perspectives

Next, it's time to shift your perspective. Consider alternative viewpoints that might contradict or balance the self-doubt you've identified. Think about your accomplishments, positive qualities, and the times when you've proven your abilities. Write these down as well.

_____

_____

_____

_____

_____

Step 4: Reframe the Self-Doubt

Now, it's time to reframe that self-doubt into a positive, empowering belief. Take the self-doubt you wrote down in Step 1 and transform it into a statement that empowers and motivates you. Here are some examples to guide you:

◆ From "I'm not good enough" to "I am continually growing and learning, and my worth is inherent."

◆ From "I'm always a failure" to "I embrace failures as opportunities for growth and resilience."

Craft your own empowering belief that resonates with you personally. Make sure it feels positive, authentic, and attainable.

_____

_____

_____

_____

▮ Step 5: Repeat and Reinforce

To truly integrate this cognitive reframing into your life, repeat your empowering belief daily. Write it down, post it in visible places, and say it to yourself with conviction. Whenever the old self-doubt resurfaces, consciously replace it with your new, empowering belief.

Constructing Confidence from the Ruins of Doubt

Let's start by reframing your perspective on self-doubt. Instead of viewing it as a weakness, consider it as a valuable source of self-inquiry. When you doubt yourself, it's your inner self whispering that there are unaddressed aspects of your past, unhealed wounds, or limiting beliefs waiting to be explored. Think of self-doubt as a spotlight, shining a light on areas in need of healing and transformation.

Practical Exercises for Self-Inquiry and Transformation

- **Journaling:** Write down the moments when self-doubt creeps in. Dig deep and think of the thoughts and feelings associated with it. Ask yourself questions like:

  » "What triggered this doubt?"

» "What past experiences might be influencing these feel-ings?"

» "What do I fear or believe about myself in this situation?"

_____

_____

_____

_____

_____

- ◆ **Mindfulness meditation:** Practice mindfulness to observe your self-doubt without judgment. As you sit quietly, bring your attention to the doubts as they arise. Observe them like leaves blowing in the wind, acknowledging their presence without reacting. This practice can help you detach from self-doubt and gain a deeper understanding of its origins.

- ◆ **Inner child work:** Often, self-doubt stems from childhood experiences. Use guided inner child meditation or visualization exercises offered earlier in this book to connect with your younger self. Offer love, compassion, and healing to the child within you who may still carry wounds from the past.

 ### Self-Doubt to Confidence Worksheet

 Before we can conquer self-doubt, we must first understand its grip on our lives. Take a moment to evaluate your levels of self-doubt in various areas. Use the scales, questionnaires, or prompts provided in the worksheet to pinpoint where self-doubt is most prevalent for you.

Self-Doubt to Confidence Worksheet

On a scale of 1 to 10, rate your self-doubt in your personal relationships.

1   2   3   4   5   6   7   8   9   10
○   ○   ○   ○   ○   ○   ○   ○   ○   ○

1 (No self-doubt) to 10 (Overwhelming self-doubt)

How does self-doubt affect your professional life? Describe specific instances or situations.

_____

_____

_____

_____

_____

In what situations do you find your self-esteem plummeting? (e.g., social gatherings, public speaking, meeting new people)

1. _____

2. _____

3. _____

4. _____

5. _____

Are there any recurring negative thoughts or beliefs that contribute to your self-doubt? Write them down.

1. _____

2. _____

3. _____

4. _____

5. _____

Challenging Negative Beliefs

In Chapter 3, we discussed how to challenge negative beliefs. Now, let's take it a step further. Here's an advanced exercise to help you identify and challenge those deeply ingrained negative beliefs:

Write down the one most recurring negative belief that affects your life.

Negative Belief: _____

_____

_____

Ask yourself, "Is this belief true or is it coming from a shadow place?" Challenge its validity.

_____

_____

_____

What alternative, empowering beliefs counteract this negative one. Write them down.

_____

_____

_____

For each empowering belief, list actions you can take to reinforce it in your daily life.

Action 1: _____

Action 2: _____

Action 3: _____

Action 4: _____

Action 5: _____

Building Confidence Through Action

Now, let's turn theory into practice. Confidence is not built solely through introspection; it thrives in action. Here are some action-oriented exercises to help you step outside your comfort zone.

Choose one situation or activity that triggers your self-doubt.
Commit to facing it head-on within the next week.

Write down your experiences and emotions before, during, and after taking action.

Experiences & Emotions
BEFORE Facing Your Self-Doubt Trigger:

_____

_____

_____

_____

Experiences & Emotions
DURING Facing Your Self-Doubt Trigger:

_____

_____

_____

_____

Experiences & Emotions
AFTER Facing Your Self-Doubt Trigger:

_____

_____

_____

_____

Reflection and Growth

Throughout your journey, reflection is key to progress. Use these journal prompts to reflect on your growth, setbacks, and insights.

What have you learned about yourself since you started this workbook?

_____

_____

_____

_____

_____

How have your perceptions of self-doubt evolved?

_____

_____

_____

_____

_____

What actions have you taken that made you feel more confident and self-assured?

_____

_____

_____

_____

_____

_____

_____

_____

Maintenance Plan

Finally, let's ensure that your newfound confidence continues to flourish.

✓ Create a maintenance plan that aligns with your self-care needs and reinforces your progress.

✓ Set regular self-care activities in a calendar or schedule. Open the calendar app on your phone or make a physical one and assign a color to self-care. Be sure you commit that color to enough time during that month for self-care.

✓ Identify potential triggers for self-doubt and how you'll address them proactively.

✓ Outline a support system of friends and mentors who can provide guidance when needed.

As you've embarked on this profound exploration of the chatter within your own mind, you've taken monumental strides toward healing and self-discovery. You've learned to face self-doubt head-on, challenge the relentless negativity that often plagues your thoughts, and connect with the enigmatic depths of your shadow self.

In the upcoming chapter, we will explore the advanced dynamics of relationships, unveiling how your newfound mastery over your internal world can be harnessed to enhance empathy, foster forgiveness, and enable effective communication.

CHAPTER 5
TRANSFORMING HURT INTO HEALING - THE ART OF FORGIVENESS

Transforming Hurt Into Healing - The Art of Forgiveness

> **66**
>
> *Forgiveness does not change the past, but it does enlarge the future. —Paul Boese*
>
> **99**

In this chapter, we explore the intricate tapestry of relationships—those complex, beautiful, and often perplexing connections that define so much of our human experience. Here, in the realm of our interactions with others, we often discover the most profound reflections of our inner selves.

You may have realized that your past experiences and unhealed wounds have a significant impact on your relationships. Perhaps you've observed patterns of behavior and communication that leave you feeling stuck in a cycle of frustration or hurt.

In this chapter, we will shine a light on the essential elements that underpin thriving relationships: empathy, forgiveness, and clear communication. These are the cornerstones of emotional intelligence and the keys to unlocking a world of connection and understanding.

Enhancing Empathy in Relationships

Empathy, in its essence, is the remarkable ability not only to understand but also to share the feelings of another person. It transcends mere sympathy, allowing you to step into someone else's shoes and experience their world through their eyes and emotions. Now, why is this a cornerstone of your shadow work? Let's dive in.

Understanding on a Deeper Level

Empathy is the key that unlocks the door to understanding others on a profound level. As you continue your shadow work, you'll realize that your own struggles and challenges have shaped you. And just as you seek understanding and healing for your own wounds, so too do others. When you can empathize, you're better equipped to comprehend the experiences and emotions that mold someone's character.

Your journey into the shadows is about more than just self-discovery; it's about embracing your true self and letting others see that authenticity too. Empathy plays a vital role here. When you can empathize with someone, it fosters a sense of trust and closeness. Your ability to connect on a deeper emotional level enables you to build bonds that are resilient, authentic, and enduring.

Now, let's discuss how shadow traits can sometimes block empathy and how recognizing these traits within ourselves can be transformative.

To truly embrace empathy, we must first visit our shadow self—the hidden aspects of our personality, experiences, and emotions that we often suppress or deny. These shadows can act as a defensive barrier between us and our loved ones, hindering our ability to express ourselves authentically.

When triggered, these shadow traits can lead to misunderstandings, conflicts, and emotional distance within our relationships. The lack of insight into our shadows can make it challenging to rectify these situations, leading to recurring disputes.

However, understanding your own shadows and acknowledging them is the key to unlocking deeper empathy. When you work through your shadow side, you become better equipped to comprehend the shadows in others. This newfound awareness allows you to approach conflicts and challenges in your relationships with compassion and a genuine desire to understand, ultimately fostering healthier, more profound connections.

 ### Exercise: Empathy Expansion

The objective of this exercise is to expand your capacity for empathy by reflecting on recent interactions and understanding the emotions of others involved.

◆ Select a recent encounter or conversation with someone significant in your life. It could be a friend, family member, colleague, or partner.

◆ Take a moment to recall the details of this interaction. Think about what was said, body language, and the overall emotional atmosphere. Try to remember how you felt during the conversation.

◆ Try to envision yourself as the other person. Imagine how they might have felt during the interaction. Consider their perspective, emotions, and potential triggers. Were they happy, sad, frustrated, or confused?

 Use the empathy quiz questions below as a guide to assess your empathy in this situation. Answer each question honestly based on your reflection.

I often experience sadness when those in my proximity are also feeling down.

strongly disagree   disagree   neutral   agree   strongly agree

○   ○   ○   ○   ○

Prior to offering criticism, I make an effort to envision how I'd feel if I were in their shoes.

strongly disagree   disagree   neutral   agree   strongly agree

○   ○   ○   ○   ○

Understanding what brings happiness to my friends can be challenging for me.

strongly disagree   disagree   neutral   agree   strongly agree

○   ○   ○   ○   ○

Witnessing someone being treated disrespectfully deeply disturbs me.

strongly disagree   disagree   neutral   agree   strongly agree

○   ○   ○   ○   ○

When someone else is feeling enthusiastic, I often find myself sharing in that excitement.

strongly disagree	disagree	neutral	agree	strongly agree
○	○	○	○	○

I have tender, concerned feelings for people less fortunate than me.

strongly disagree	disagree	neutral	agree	strongly agree
○	○	○	○	○

I sometimes find it difficult to see things from the other person's point of view.

strongly disagree	disagree	neutral	agree	strongly agree
○	○	○	○	○

I notice that I am sensitive to and attuned to the moods of others.

strongly disagree	disagree	neutral	agree	strongly agree
○	○	○	○	○

When I am confident in my correctness about something, I tend not to invest much time in listening to others' counterarguments.

strongly disagree	disagree	neutral	agree	strongly agree
○	○	○	○	○

When someone shares an event that brought them joy, I can readily comprehend why that experience made them happy.

strongly disagree	disagree	neutral	agree	strongly agree
○	○	○	○	○

I try to look at everybody's side of a disagreement before I make a decision.

strongly disagree   disagree   neutral   agree   strongly agree
○   ○   ○   ○   ○

I become irritated when someone cries.

strongly disagree   disagree   neutral   agree   strongly agree
○   ○   ○   ○   ○

It is effortless for me to come up with scenarios that would bring happiness to my friends.

strongly disagree   disagree   neutral   agree   strongly agree
○   ○   ○   ○   ○

At times, I make an effort to gain a better understanding of my friends by envisioning situations from their point of view.

strongly disagree   disagree   neutral   agree   strongly agree
○   ○   ○   ○   ○

I feel a strong inclination to lend a hand when I come across someone who is feeling upset.

strongly disagree   disagree   neutral   agree   strongly agree
○   ○   ○   ○   ○

Evaluate your empathy: After completing the quiz, assess your empathy level in this specific interaction. Were there moments where you demonstrated strong empathy? Were there areas where you could improve?

_____

_____

_____

_____

_____

_____

Share and discuss: If you feel comfortable and the situation allows, consider sharing your insights with the person involved in the interaction. Engaging in an open and empathetic conversation can deepen your connection and understanding of each other.

Advanced Communication Strategies

Communication is the lifeblood of human connection, and it plays a pivotal role in shadow work. How you communicate with yourself and others can either perpetuate old wounds or pave the way for profound healing and transformation.

> **Begin by examining your communication habits. Ask yourself the following questions.**

Are you passive-aggressive, avoidant, or confrontational?

_____

_____

Do you often suppress your true feelings and thoughts?

_____

_____

Pay attention to the unspoken messages in your interactions. Sometimes, what isn't said carries more weight than what is. Hidden fears, insecurities, and unresolved issues can manifest in subtle cues and undertones during conversations.

When you find yourself reacting strongly to someone's words or actions, take a moment to explore why you're triggered. These emotional reactions can be gateways to uncovering deeper wounds and beliefs within your shadow self.

Techniques for Clear and Mindful Communication

- **Active listening:** To uncover hidden aspects of your shadow self, practice active listening. When engaged in a conversation, focus not only on the words but also on the speaker's emotions, body language, and tone. Ask open-ended questions so they feel they can be open and honest.

- **Empathetic responses:** Respond empathetically when someone shares their thoughts or feelings. Empathy fosters a safe space for open communication. You can say, "What can I do to help," or "Tell me more about what's going on for you."

- **Use "I" statements:** When expressing your own thoughts and emotions, use "I" statements to take ownership of your feelings. For example, say, "I feel hurt when..." instead of "You hurt me when..." This helps avoid blame and promotes understanding.

- **Nonviolent communication:** NVC is all about how we communicate openly and empathetically with others. It involves four key components: observations, feelings, needs, and requests. While all four are important, the heart of empathetic connection really lies in understanding feelings and needs. Practicing NVC means learning to distinguish these core components from judgments, interpretations, and demands. It's about embodying the mindset that these components represent. This way, we can express ourselves and listen to others in a way that fosters understanding and deepens connections. It's about helping everyone involved get their needs met. NVC supports our well-being and helps us navigate our actions and responses in a more authentic and compassionate way (Kashtan & Kashtan, n.d.).

- **Journaling for clarity:** Journaling can be a powerful tool to examine your communication patterns. Write down your conversations, your emotional reactions, and any insights gained during your interactions. This process can reveal hidden beliefs and emotions.

By integrating these communication strategies into your daily life, you'll not only enhance your relationships but also gain a deeper understanding of your shadow self.

As you continue your exploration, you'll find that clear and mindful communication is a bridge to the uncharted territories of your psyche, where profound healing and growth await.

 ## Exercise: The Mirror of Authentic Communication

Objective: To practice open and honest communication with a trusted partner or friend in order to explore and heal deep-seated emotional wounds and practice communication skills.

Instructions:

1. **Choose your partner:** Select a trustworthy friend or partner who is willing to engage in this exercise with you. It's essential to pick someone who can provide emotional support and maintain confidentiality.

2. **Set the stage:** Find a quiet and comfortable space where you can have an uninterrupted conversation. Consider lighting a candle or playing soothing music to create a relaxed atmosphere.

3. **Roles:** Decide who will be the "Speaker" and who will be the "Listener" for the first round. You will switch roles later.

4. **Speaker's turn:** The Speaker begins by sharing a specific emotional issue or past experience they want to explore and heal. Encourage them to be as detailed and honest as possible. While speaking, the Speaker should focus on their emotions, thoughts, and physical sensations related to the issue. Encourage them to express themselves fully, without judgment or self-censorship. The Listener's role is to actively listen and offer validation, empathy, and support. They should avoid interrupting or providing solutions at this stage. The Speaker continues until they feel they have expressed their feelings and thoughts thoroughly.

5. **Switch roles:** After the Speaker feels they have sufficiently expressed themselves, switch roles. The Listener will now become the Speaker, and vice versa.

6. **Reflect and discuss:** Now that both partners have had the opportunity to share, take some time to discuss the experience. Ask open-ended questions like:

   » How did it feel to express your emotions openly?

   » What insights did you gain about the root of your feelings?

   » Did you notice any patterns or triggers in your emotions?

7. **Practice empathy and feedback:** As the Listener, provide feedback and insights based on what you heard from the Speaker. Offer your perspective on their emotions and thought processes. Remember to be empathetic and non-judgmental in your feedback. Use "I" statements to take ownership.

8. **Set intentions for healing:** Each partner should set an intention for healing and personal communication growth based on the insights gained during the exercise.

9. **Repeat and reflect:** Over the course of several weeks, continue to engage in this exercise with your partner or friend. Rotate roles and explore different communication strategies.

10. **Journaling:** After each session, participants should journal their feelings, insights, and any changes in communication they feel could help in the next round. This will help track progress and identify recurring patterns.

Forgiveness as an Advanced Practice

Forgiveness is a powerful tool in your arsenal for healing and growth. It's not just about letting go of past hurts; it's about releasing the chains that bind you to those wounds and allowing your inner light to shine even brighter. Let's break down the shadow work aspects of forgiveness.

The Shadow of Grudges

Holding onto grudges can be a shadow trait that keeps you stuck in the past. It's like carrying a heavy burden that drags you down. The truth is, holding onto resentment and anger doesn't harm the person who wronged you; it only keeps you imprisoned in negativity.

> **Take a moment to reflect on the grudges you may be holding onto. Write them down and how they are affecting your life.**

_____

_____

_____

_____

_____

_____

Forgiving Yourself

Self-forgiveness is a critical step in this journey. We all make mistakes, and often, we are our harshest critics.

> **Reflect on the moments in your life when you've been hard on yourself. Write down instances where self-forgiveness is needed. Remember, we will delve even deeper into self-forgiveness in Chapter 7.**

_____

_____

_____

_____

_____

Forgiving Others

Forgiving others is not about condoning their actions or reconciling with them. It's about releasing the emotional grip they have on you. Acknowledge that forgiveness doesn't mean you have to be on good terms with the person who hurt you. You can take all the time you need to be comfortable with this process. There's no definite timeline for forgiveness.

Complete these journal prompts for self-reflection:

What grudges am I currently holding onto, and how are they affecting my well-being?

_____
_____
_____
_____
_____

What moments in my life have I been too hard on myself? How can I begin the process of self-forgiveness?

_____
_____
_____
_____
_____
_____

Are there people in my life whom I need to forgive, even if it doesn't lead to reconciliation? What emotions are tied to these individuals?

Remember, forgiveness is a journey, not a destination. It's a gift you give to yourself, allowing you to release the past and embrace a future filled with healing and growth.

 ## *Exercise: Forgiveness Flowchart*

 A Forgiveness Flowchart is a visual tool that helps you map out your path to forgiveness for a particular hurtful event or situation. It provides clarity by breaking down the complex process of forgiveness into manageable steps. This tool will help you understand the various components involved in forgiveness, allowing you to explore your feelings, thoughts, and potential pathways toward letting go and healing.

Begin by choosing a specific event or situation from your past that still lingers in your mind, causing emotional distress. It might be an argument, a betrayal, a loss, or any experience that continues to affect you negatively. Write it down.

_____

_____

_____

_____

_____

List and describe the emotions that this event triggers within you. Be honest and thorough. How does this event make you feel? Explore the anger, sadness, guilt, shame, or any other emotions that come up.

_____

_____

_____

_____

_____

Now, dig deeper. Try to identify the root causes of these emotions. Ask yourself questions like:

» Why does this event affect me so deeply?

_____

_____

_____

» What past experiences or beliefs may be contributing to these emotions?

_____

_____

_____

Understanding the source of your feelings is crucial to your healing journey.

In the heart of your Forgiveness Flowchart, list branches that represent potential paths to forgiveness. These could include self-forgiveness, understanding the other person's perspective, seeking closure, or letting go of the need for retribution. Be creative and open to various possibilities.

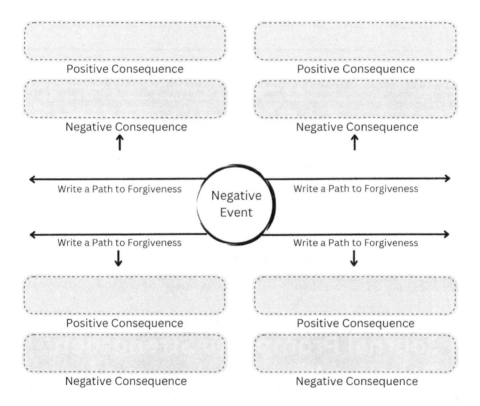

Along each path, note down the potential consequences, both positive and negative. How might forgiving or not forgiving affect your mental and emotional well-being, relationships, and overall life satisfaction?

Take a moment to reflect on the Forgiveness Flowchart you've created. Are there any paths that resonate with you more than others? What insights have you gained about yourself and your emotions? Finally, commit to taking one small step toward forgiveness, even if it's just the intention to explore this path further.

_____

_____

_____

_____

_____

Journal Prompts to Strengthen Relationships

Each prompt is designed to encourage empathy, forgiveness, and communication skills within relationships. Let's embark on this transformative journey together with optimism, support, and a commitment to your personal growth.

Reflect on the recurring patterns in your relationships. What similarities or themes do you notice? How might your past experiences be influencing your present interactions?

_____

_____

_____

_____

_____

Think about the people who trigger strong emotional reactions in you, both positive and negative. What does this tell you about yourself and your unmet needs or unresolved wounds?

_____

_____

_____

_____

_____

Consider a challenging relationship or situation from your past. How did you contribute to the dynamics, positively or negatively? What lessons can you learn from taking responsibility for your role?

_____

_____

_____

_____

_____

Explore the concept of projection in your relationships. Can you identify instances where you projected your own insecurities or desires onto others? How did this affect the relationship dynamics?

_____

_____

_____

_____

_____

Reflect on the times when you avoided vulnerability in your relationships. What fears or insecurities were you protecting? How might embracing vulnerability lead to healthier connections?

_____

_____

_____

_____

_____

Think about someone in your life who has hurt you deeply. Can you find compassion for their own struggles and wounds? How might forgiving them contribute to your healing?

_____

_____

_____

_____

_____

Consider a recent conflict or misunderstanding in one of your relationships. How could improved communication have prevented or resolved it? What can you do to enhance your communication skills?

_____

_____

_____

_____

_____

Explore your need for control in relationships. Are there situations where you tend to be controlling? What underlying fears or insecurities drive this need, and how can you empower yourself instead?

_____
_____
_____
_____
_____
_____

Reflect on your ability to set and maintain boundaries. How do healthy boundaries contribute to your self-worth and overall well-being? In what areas do you need to strengthen your boundaries?

_____
_____
_____
_____
_____

Envision the kind of healthy, fulfilling relationships you desire. What qualities and behaviors do you expect from yourself and others in these relationships? How can you align your actions with this vision?

_____
_____
_____
_____
_____

Affirmations to Strengthen Relationship Skills

 These affirmations are designed to foster empathy, forgiveness, and clear communication in your interactions with others. I encourage you to use these affirmations regularly as part of your deep shadow work journey:

Empathy affirmations:

- » "I am committed to understanding the feelings and perspectives of others."

- » "Empathy is my superpower, and I use it to connect deeply with those around me."

- » "I approach every interaction with an open heart and a willingness to listen."

- » "I see the beauty in understanding the emotions behind every action."

 Forgiveness affirmations:

- » "I release the weight of past grievances and embrace the freedom of forgiveness."

- » "Forgiving others is a gift I give myself, liberating my heart and soul."

- » "I understand that forgiveness doesn't justify actions; it simply allows me to move forward."

- » "I choose to forgive and let go, knowing it paves the way for healing."

 Clear communication affirmations:

- » "I express myself honestly and authentically, fostering open communication."

- » "Clarity, in my words, leads to understanding and deeper connections."

- » "I listen actively, seeking to comprehend rather than simply respond."

- » "I value the power of words to build bridges and strengthen relationships."

Relationship Affirmations:

- » "My relationships are a source of love, growth, and mutual support."
- » "Every challenge in a relationship is an opportunity for growth and deeper connection."
- » "I create a safe space for vulnerability and emotional expression in my relationships."
- » "I attract positive, loving, and nurturing relationships into my life."

 Self-reflection affirmations:

- » "I take time to reflect on my own actions and their impact on my relationships."
- » "Self-awareness is the key to my personal growth and better relationships."
- » "I embrace the journey of self-discovery, knowing it enhances my ability to connect with others."
- » "I am open to change and growth, both for myself and within my relationships."

Again, I encourage you to repeat these daily and contemplate their deeper meaning. These affirmations are tools to help you cultivate the mindset and habits necessary for nurturing healthy, fulfilling relationships.

Give yourself the credit you deserve for completing this chapter on relationships and the powerful tools of empathy, forgiveness, and clear communication. You've taken significant strides in your journey of deep subconscious exploration and emotional mastery. By delving into these topics, you're already on the path to transforming your connections with others and, ultimately, yourself. Now, as we transition into the next chapter, we'll explore the intricate relationship between fear, anxiety, and depression and how they are connected to your shadow work. These emotions often hold the keys to unlocking your deepest wounds and untapped potential. So, get ready to uncover the hidden facets of your psyche and continue your profound inner work.

CHAPTER 6
THE DARK SHADOWS

The Dark Shadows

> *He who is not every day conquering some fear has not learned the secret of life. —**Ralph Waldo Emerson***

Fear, anxiety, and depression have been formidable companions on your journey thus far. They've whispered doubts, triggered old wounds, and led you down dark alleys of the mind. But what if I told you these emotions could be your greatest catalysts for growth and transformation? That's precisely what this chapter is all about.

Together, we will transform fear into courage, anxiety into resilience, and depression into profound self-compassion. You'll understand the intricate connections between these emotions and your shadow and learn how to use them as powerful tools for personal growth.

The Deeper Dance with Fear and Anxiety

You've probably come across the question: "What would you do if you weren't afraid?" It's a powerful inquiry, but today, let's elevate it to a whole new level: "Who would you be if you weren't afraid?" Imagine, for a moment, a life where fear and anxiety no longer held you back. Envision the freedom to be your authentic self, unapologetically and without reservation.

 The journey to overcoming your fears is not just about facing them head-on; it's about discovering your true self in the process. When you know who you are at your core, you can answer life's essential questions with unwavering clarity and honesty:

What do you love?

1. _____

2. _____

3. _____

4. _____

5. _____

List what you consider your biggest strengths and weaknesses.

Strengths

1. _____
2. _____
3. _____
4. _____
5. _____

Weaknesses

1. _____
2. _____
3. _____
4. _____
5. _____

Write down who truly inspires you.

1. _____

2. _____

3. _____

4. _____

5. _____

What is your biggest dream?

_____
_____
_____
_____
_____

What do you want out of life—really want?

_____
_____
_____
_____
_____

Can you identify what is working for you currently in your life and what isn't?

What is Working

1. _____

2. _____

3. _____

4. _____

5. _____

What isn't Working

1. _____
2. _____
3. _____
4. _____
5. _____

These may seem like straightforward questions, but they often stir inner turmoil. People frequently respond based on societal expectations or what they believe they "should" say. For example, when asked what we want out of life, we may feel we are expected to say, "Good health and peace." In all honesty, you may want to be rich. When answering, "What do you love," society may place pressure on answering things like our children, our spouse, and so forth. When we take the fear out of what others may view us as, we will answer honestly and say, "I love vacationing alone" or "I love not having children." Fear plays a pivotal role in this evasion of self-discovery.

 I want you to answer the questions above again, leaving fear out of the equation.

Fear manifests in various ways, each holding us back from embracing our true selves:

♦ **Fear of weakness:** It's natural to hesitate when facing your flaws. No one wants to confront their imperfections. However, recognizing your weaknesses is the first step toward transforming them into strengths.

♦ **Fear of vulnerability:** Knowing your true self requires exposing your authentic self to others, risking rejection. But vulnerability is the gateway to profound connections and meaningful relationships.

◆ **Fear of letting others down:** What if your true self contradicts others' expectations? This fear may make you think it's easier not to seek your true self. Yet, by not doing so, you deny yourself the happiness you deserve.

◆ **Fear of change:** Embracing your true self may necessitate changes in your life. Change can be intimidating, but stagnation can be even scarier. The choice is between remaining stuck or taking a leap toward a brighter future.

Fear is not an absolute truth; it's a construct of your mind. To discover your true self, you must confront and conquer these fears. When you expose them for the falsehoods they are, your true self will emerge, emboldened and unburdened. You'll realize it's not only okay to be who you are but that the fears were holding you back instead of protecting you.

Overcoming your fears is an essential part of the journey to your true self. Remember, your true self is your key to creating a life that aligns with your deepest desires and a life you truly deserve. Embrace this process with courage and determination, for the rewards are nothing less than transformational.

 Exercise: Fear Immersion

 Step 1: Identify Your Fear

Start by identifying a specific fear that has been holding you back. It could be fear of public speaking, confrontation, vulnerability, or any other fear that resonates with you. Write down this fear.

_____

_____

_____

 Step 2: Set Clear Goals

Define your goals for this fear immersion exercise. What do you hope to achieve by facing this fear? Is it to build confidence, overcome a past trauma, or simply reduce anxiety? Be clear about your intentions.

1. _____

2. _____

3. _____

Step 3: Gradual Exposure

Begin exposing yourself to the feared situation in a controlled and gradual manner. For example, if your fear is public speaking, start by speaking in front of a mirror. Progress to speaking in front of a trusted friend or family member. Gradually increase the size of your audience as you become more comfortable.

Step 4: Journal Your Experience

After each exposure session, take time to journal your emotional responses. Be brutally honest with yourself. How did you feel before, during, and after the exposure? What thoughts and physical sensations arose? Write down any insights or realizations you had.

Date:_____ Fear:_____

Event:_____

_____

Before Exposure	During Exposure	After Exposure
Thoughts	Thoughts	Thoughts
Physical Sensations	Physical Sensations	Physical Sensations

Date:_____ Event:_____

Before Exposure	During Exposure	After Exposure
Thoughts	Thoughts	Thoughts
Physical Sensations	Physical Sensations	Physical Sensations

Step 5: Reflect and Adjust

Review your entries regularly to track your progress. Are you noticing any changes in your emotional responses or thought patterns? Reflect on what you've learned and adjust your exposure sessions accordingly. You may need to push your boundaries further or give yourself more time as needed.

_____
_____
_____
_____
_____

Remember, this exercise is an advanced technique and may bring up intense emotions. Approach it with self-compassion and patience.

The Depths of Depression

Depression, as you may have experienced, is not just a random occurrence or an unwelcome visitor. Instead, it can be seen as a beacon, a signal from your inner self that something profound is in need of attention and healing. It is an opportunity to embark on a journey of self-discovery, to unearth the buried treasures within your psyche, and to ultimately create the life you truly deserve.

First, let's shift our perspective on depression. Instead of viewing it solely as a heavy burden or an enemy to be defeated, consider it as a messenger from your deepest self. Depression often arises when unresolved issues or neglected aspects of your identity cry out for acknowledgment. It is your inner self's way of saying, "Pay attention to me. I need your love, understanding, and healing."

 ### *Recognizing Patterns in Depressive Episodes*

Let's explore the patterns in depressive episodes that can serve as invitations to explore deeper shadow aspects of the self:

♦ **Recurring triggers:** Pay close attention to the situations or circumstances that tend to trigger your depressive episodes. These triggers often hold clues about unresolved issues or unacknowledged aspects of your shadow self. For example, if social interactions consistently trigger feelings of inadequacy or self-doubt, it may be an invitation to explore deeper feelings of unworthiness.

- **Emotional resonance:** When you're in the midst of depression, take note of the emotions that arise. Do you feel overwhelming sadness, anger, or fear? These intense emotions are often connected to buried experiences or aspects of your identity that are seeking acknowledgment. Exploring the root causes of these emotions can lead you to hidden shadows.

- **Repetitive thought patterns:** Depressive episodes frequently come with repetitive, negative thought patterns. These thoughts might revolve around self-criticism, feelings of hopelessness, or a sense of powerlessness. These cognitive patterns are often tied to unresolved wounds from the past, and they can provide valuable insights into the deeper layers of your shadow self.

- **Relationship dynamics:** Your relationships can be mirrors reflecting aspects of your shadow self. Notice if there are recurring themes or conflicts in your relationships that seem to align with your depressive episodes. For example, if you consistently attract partners who are emotionally unavailable, it might be connected to a fear of intimacy or abandonment that requires exploration.

- **Self-Sabotage:** When depression strikes, it can lead to self-sabotaging behaviors such as procrastination, isolation, or self-destructive habits. These actions may be attempts to cope with or avoid facing unresolved issues or shadow aspects. Identifying these behaviors and their underlying causes can lead you toward healing.

- **Loss of interest and passion:** Depression often saps your motivation and enthusiasm for life. Consider the activities, passions, or hobbies that you once enjoyed but have lost interest in. The loss of these interests may signal a disconnect from parts of your authentic self that you've suppressed or denied.

◆ **Physical symptoms:** Some people experience physical symptoms along with depression, such as fatigue, headaches, or gastrointestinal issues. These physical manifestations can be connected to emotional or psychological wounds that are waiting to be addressed.

◆ **Dreams and nightmares:** Your dreams and nightmares can provide a window into your subconscious mind. Pay attention to recurring themes or symbols in your dreams, as they can shed light on unconscious material that is surfacing through your depressive episodes.

Recognizing these patterns requires a level of self-awareness and introspection. As you explore these aspects during your depressive episodes, remember to approach them with self-compassion. The goal is not to blame yourself but to understand and heal.

 ## *From Stagnation to Transformation*

The magic of engaging with depression through the lens of shadow work lies in the potential for profound growth and transformation. Instead of remaining stuck in the cycle of despair, you'll embark on a journey of self-empowerment and healing. You'll gain the tools and insights needed to address the root causes of your emotional pain, allowing you to break free from the chains of old patterns and beliefs. You'll learn to reframe your cognitive processes, unlocking a new level of emotional mastery. The goal is not merely to cope with depression but to confront it head-on, armed with advanced methods rooted in self-awareness, self-compassion, and profound transformation.

Exercise: Shadow Lessons Journaling

Step 1: Identify the Feeling

Think back to a recent depressive episode. Take a moment to recall the emotions and thoughts that surrounded you during that challenging time. Write down what you felt and thought, no matter how uncomfortable it may be. Be honest with yourself.

_____

_____

_____

_____

_____

Step 2: Connect to the Shadow

Now, let's dig deeper. Reflect on which aspects of your shadow these feelings might be connected to. Consider whether these emotions could be linked to a part of yourself you've been neglecting or suppressing. The shadow is often comprised of the rejected, unseen, or denied aspects of our personality. What part of your shadow is manifesting in these depressive feelings?

_____

_____

_____

_____

_____

Step 3: Extract the Lesson

Here's where the real work begins. Ask yourself what your depression is trying to communicate. What is the underlying lesson hidden within these painful emotions? Depression is not merely a random occurrence; it often points to unmet needs, unresolved traumas, or unexpressed desires.

What does this depression want you to acknowledge about yourself?

1. _____

_____

2. _____

_____

3. _____

_____

What needs or desires have you been neglecting?

1. _____

2. _____

3. _____

4. _____

5. _____

Are there past experiences or traumas that this depression is connected to?

1. _____

_____

2. _____

_____

3. _____

_____

How might understanding these lessons foster a deeper connection to yourself and instigate change in your life?

_____

_____

_____

_____

_____

As you explore these questions, be patient and compassionate with yourself. Healing is a gradual process, and uncovering shadow lessons can be intense. However, remember that you have the strength and resilience to face your shadows and emerge stronger than ever.

Once you've completed this exercise, take some time to reflect on your findings. Consider how you can use this newfound knowledge to create healthier habits and align your life with your true self.

Harnessing Emotional Energy

In your journey to heal, you may have experienced the silent but blatant message, "My feelings don't matter." It's a message often ingrained in those who grew up in environments of childhood emotional neglect. You learned to adapt by walling off your emotions, but in doing so, you distanced yourself from your true self.

The mark emotional neglect leaves can be significant, but it need not last a lifetime. You can reconnect with your feelings and use them as powerful sources of energy, motivation, and connection. To harness emotional energy, you must first acknowledge and welcome your feelings. Emotions underpin everything you do, and it's time to turn inward and listen to their valuable messages.

- **Daily practice:** Be mindful of your feelings. Identify and write down your feelings three times a day.

Pushing down your feelings can lead to a loss of self-trust and reliance on the opinions of others. It's time to reestablish your connection with your inner guidance. Be the first and last person you go to for guidance before making any decision. By becoming more in tune with your own feelings, you'll gain the confidence to make decisions you can trust.

- **Daily practice:** Before any decision you make, be the first and last person you go to for guidance.

Discovering your interests and passions is a thrilling part of your recovery journey. Childhood emotional neglect may have pushed down the joy you deserve, but it's never too late to rekindle it. Your brain can adapt and develop, even in adulthood. Start by keeping a journal of your likes and dislikes and incorporate things that bring you joy into your daily routine.

◆ **Daily practice:** Keep a journal of your likes and dislikes. Incorporate things that give you joy into your routine.

Without proper emotional awareness, you may feel overwhelmed or scattered. It's time to take control of your emotions and manage your impulses effectively. Train your brain to exercise agency over your actions and reactions. Each day, challenge yourself to do one small thing you don't want to do but should or stop yourself from doing something you want to do but shouldn't.

◆ **Daily practice:** Every day, do one small thing you don't want to do (but should do), or stop yourself from doing something you want to do (but shouldn't).

Setting boundaries is an essential aspect of healthy relationships. It takes strength to say "no" when you've been conditioned to believe it's wrong or selfish. As you identify your emotions more clearly, setting boundaries becomes easier. Before you set a boundary, turn your attention inward and consider what is right for you.

◆ **Daily Practice:** Try to say "no" more often. Keep track of the number of times you're able to say no.

Anger is a powerful emotion that can be harnessed for positive change. Consider these tips to redirect your anger into a force for good:

» Discover new boundaries to set.

» Focus on what truly matters.

» Use your anger as motivation.

» Channel your anger into productive action.

» Exercise to release pent-up anger.

» Stop and reflect on why you're angry.

» Identify what you can change in the situation.

» Recognize your emotional sore points.

Affirmations for Inner Strength

Here are some affirmations for inner strength that will help you tap into your newfound wisdom from your previous experiences with shadow work. These affirmations are designed to empower and inspire you to face your deepest wounds and continue your journey toward healing and personal growth:

- "I embrace my shadow self, knowing that within its depths lie the keys to my strength and transformation."

- "With every step into the darkness, I uncover more of my inner power and resilience."

- "I trust in my ability to navigate the darkest corners of my soul, for I am the light that guides my way."

- "My past wounds no longer define me; they are stepping stones on my path to healing."

- "I am worthy of the life I desire, and I have the inner strength to create it."

- "I confront my fears and insecurities with courage and self-compassion, knowing they hold the seeds of my growth."

- "Each layer of my shadow I explore brings me closer to the authentic, empowered self I am meant to be."

Exercise: Shadow Strength Cards

Here's a set of shadow strength cards with personalized affirmations to use as a starting point. Please visit AdvancedShadow.LeighWHart.com to access printable blank cards where you can write these affirmations and make them your own:

- "I am not defined by my past. I am defined by my ability to learn, grow, and heal."

- "I am worthy of love, forgiveness, and compassion, both from others and from myself."

- "I embrace the darkness within me, knowing that it holds the key to my deepest transformation."

- "I release the need for perfection and embrace my imperfections as part of my unique beauty."

- "I trust in my inner strength to guide me through the toughest storms of life."

- "I am not alone in my journey. I have the support and understanding of those who care for me."

- "I allow myself to feel and express my emotions freely, knowing that they are a natural part of my existence."

- "I release the need to control everything and surrender to the flow of life."

- "I am resilient and capable of overcoming any obstacle that comes my way."

- "I am the author of my own story, and I choose to write a narrative filled with love, joy, and growth."

Feel free to modify or personalize these affirmations to better resonate with your unique experiences and challenges. Personalizing these cards will make them even more effective in times of overwhelm, providing a powerful tool for self-support and empowerment.

Fear, Anxiety, and Depression as Teachers

I would like to explore the profound teachings that fear, anxiety, and depression have to offer. Instead of viewing these emotions as adversaries, let's see them as invaluable teachers who can guide us toward personal growth and emotional mastery.

 ## Fear as a Teacher

Fear is often misunderstood as a roadblock, but in reality, it's a sign on the path of growth. When fear appears, it's an indication that you're moving beyond your comfort zone into uncharted territory. Embracing fear means embracing growth. Remember, growth may be uncomfortable, but it paves the way for a better and brighter version of yourself.

- **Distinguishing between perception and reality:** Often, our imagination tends to amplify worst-case scenarios, needlessly triggering anxiety. In many instances, the things we fear are far less formidable than our imaginations lead us to believe. As you reflect on past fears, you'll likely recognize that many of them appeared less intimidating in reality. Therefore, always inquire, "What's the most favorable outcome?"

- **Cultivate positive thought patterns:** Instead of fixating on the worst-case scenarios, redirect your focus towards the best possible results. Negative thinking only reinforces fear and pessimism in our lives. Understand that positive thinking isn't mere wishful thinking; it's a potent force that shapes our reality. Use your thoughts to construct a positive universe.

- **Unveil your inner resilience:** Confronting fear head-on cultivates substantial personal strength and self-assurance. Recall the instances when you confronted fear and emerged victorious. These triumphs, whether significant or minor, expand your comfort zone and unveil your genuine capabilities. Similar to the practice of yoga, overcoming fear can reveal your remarkable inner strength.

- **Embrace fear as a natural companion:** Fear is an integral facet of life, and there's no need to eradicate it. It accompanies you on your journey toward greatness. Remarkably, some of the best decisions are made in the presence of fear. Embrace it, learn to cope with it, and continue progressing despite its presence. Fear serves as an indicator that you're on the path to becoming a more remarkable version of yourself.

Anxiety as a Teacher

Anxiety can be unpredictable, but resisting it only intensifies it. Learn to flow with it, accepting that progress and success don't follow a single path. Listening to your own needs and going with the flow of your mental health is a powerful step in your healing journey.

- **Starting anew is perfectly acceptable:** Anxiety may create the illusion of regression, but, in truth, it presents an opportunity for personal growth. Even small steps hold significance and pave the way for profound transformations. Have faith in the journey, welcome change, and glean wisdom from each experience.

- **Be selective in your choice of companions:** Surround yourself with individuals who offer support, positivity, and authenticity. It is entirely acceptable to create distance from those who deplete your energy or fail to align with your aspirations. Your network should serve as a source of inspiration and encouragement rather than a hindrance.

♦ **The significance of embracing a straightforward and genuine existence:** Streamline your life by removing unnecessary burdens, both material and emotional. Embrace your true self and concentrate on what genuinely holds importance to you. Simplicity fosters mental clarity and a more genuine expression of your identity.

♦ **Heed your inner guidance:** Your intuition serves as a potent counsel, especially when making decisions concerning your mental well-being. Learn to distinguish it from the constant mental chatter. Place trust in your inner wisdom, for it can direct you toward the right path.

 Depression as a Teacher

Recognize that your brain often tends to interpret situations more negatively when you are experiencing depression. Acknowledge this predisposition and focus on objectively analyzing your thoughts.

♦ **Nutrition affects your emotional state:** Your food choices have a significant impact on your mental well-being. Be mindful of how various foods influence your mood, and opt for dietary choices that promote your overall health.

♦ **Sleep is vital for mental stability:** Give priority to getting sufficient sleep, as it is crucial for maintaining mental clarity and overall well-being. Your brain relies on its dedicated REM sleep hours for optimal functioning.

♦ **Gratitude cannot be imposed:** While practicing gratitude has its benefits, it should not be coerced. Allow yourself to experience moments of sadness when necessary, and let feelings of gratitude arise naturally when you are ready.

♦ **A sense of humor is essential:** Humor serves as a protective barrier between you and your distress. Laughter serves as a reminder that you still possess control and can navigate through challenging circumstances.

With the tools to face fear, anxiety, and depression, we're prepared to delve deeper into the shadow to release the grip of shame and guilt. Chapter 7 will guide you through this healing process, offering a pathway to forgiveness and self-compassion as integral parts of your shadow work journey.

CHAPTER 7
RELEASING THE CHAINS OF SHAME AND GUILT

Releasing the Chains of Shame and Guilt

> **"**
>
> *Forgiveness is the fragrance that the violet sheds on the heel that has crushed it. –Mark Twain*
>
> **"**

In this chapter, we venture into the profound realms of shame and guilt. These emotions can be some of the most potent barriers to our personal evolution. They linger in the hidden corners of our psyche, silently shaping our choices, relationships, and self-worth. But fear not, for this chapter holds the keys to releasing these burdens and transmuting them into stepping stones on your path to personal growth.

Shame and guilt often tether us to the past, chaining us to mistakes and missteps we've taken along our journey. They whisper cruel stories about our worthiness, convincing us that we are undeserving of the life we dream of. However, in this chapter, you will uncover the tools and insights needed to free yourself from this self-imposed bondage.

Our primary goal here is to guide you toward self-forgiveness. To let go of the past, not by denying it, but by embracing it with compassion and understanding. We'll explore the roots of shame and guilt, dissect their intricate patterns, and learn advanced methods to release their grip on your soul.

Let's release the shackles of shame and guilt and embrace the boundless potential that awaits. Your life of healing and growth is within reach, and I am excited to witness your continued transformation.

Understanding the Roots of Guilt and Shame

Let's tackle the intricate and often challenging territory of understanding the roots of guilt and shame. These two emotions can be incredibly powerful forces in our lives, influencing our actions, decisions, and overall well-being. To transform and heal, it's essential to not only recognize these feelings but also to trace them back to their origins, identifying the specific events or beliefs that have contributed to their presence in your life.

 ## *Tracing the Origins of Guilt and Shame*

 Begin by setting aside some dedicated time for introspection. Reflect on moments in your life when you have felt overwhelming guilt or shame. Be as specific as possible, and don't shy away from the uncomfortable memories. These emotions can often stem from childhood experiences, family dynamics, societal expectations, or personal beliefs.

_____

_____

_____

_____

_____

_____

_____

_____

_____

_____

Once you've identified these moments, consider how they have shaped your self-perception, relationships, and choices throughout your life. Can you identify recurring patterns or themes? Are there any common threads that connect these experiences?

_____

_____

_____

_____

_____

Guilt and Shame as Indicators of Disowned Parts

Understand that guilt and shame are not just negative emotions to be discarded but rather powerful indicators of disowned parts of yourself. These emotions often point to aspects of your personality, desires, or beliefs that you've suppressed or rejected due to societal pressure or fear of judgment. By acknowledging and embracing these disowned parts, you can begin to integrate them into your self-identity and achieve a more holistic sense of self.

The Shadow Self and Its Connection

Guilt and shame are intimately connected to the concept of the shadow self. The shadow self represents the hidden, unacknowledged aspects of your personality and psyche. It's the repository of unexpressed emotions, desires, and experiences. As you trace the origins of guilt and shame, you may uncover how these emotions are tied to aspects of your shadow self that you've been avoiding.

Healthy Remorse vs. Destructive Shame

It's vital to distinguish between healthy remorse and destructive shame. Healthy remorse is a constructive emotion that arises when you recognize a mistake or wrongdoing and take responsibility for it. It encourages personal growth and accountability. On the other hand, destructive shame is self-condemnation that stifles growth. It makes you believe you are fundamentally flawed and unworthy, leading to self-destructive behaviors.

As you work through your guilt and shame, strive to cultivate healthy remorse for actions that genuinely warrant it. Acknowledge your mistakes and use them as opportunities for personal growth. Simultaneously, challenge destructive shame by reframing your self-perception and embracing self-compassion.

 Exercise: Guilt and Shame Mapping

 This exercise will help you create a visual representation of these emotions and understand their impact on your life –let's get started!

 Step 1: Setting the Stage

Begin by finding a quiet, comfortable space where you can focus without distractions. Take a few deep breaths to center yourself and prepare for this deep exploration.

 Step 2: Creating Your Map

At the center of your page, draw a circle or a symbol to represent yourself. This symbolizes your core identity.

Now, use different colors to draw lines or branches extending from your core symbol, like the roots of a tree. Each branch represents a specific source or event related to your feelings of guilt and shame. Write a brief description or keyword next to each branch to label it.

Continue to branch out as needed, connecting to more specific events or beliefs that contribute to your experience of guilt and shame. These could be incidents from your past, relationships, societal pressures, or personal expectations.

▇ Step 3: Reflecting on Impact

For each branch or source you've identified, take a moment to reflect on how it has influenced your life. Write down the emotional, psychological, and behavioral impacts these sources have had on you. Be honest and open with yourself.

Ask yourself questions like:

◆ How have these feelings affected my self-esteem and self-worth?

_____

_____

_____

_____

◆ In what ways have they influenced my decisions and actions?

_____

_____

_____

_____

◆ Have I been avoiding certain opportunities or relationships due to these emotions?

_____

_____

_____

_____

▇ Step 4: Identifying Patterns

Look for patterns or common themes that emerge as you examine your guilt and shame map. Jot down any recurring triggers or situations that lead to these emotions. Recognizing patterns can provide valuable insights into the root causes of your feelings.

1. _____

2. _____

3. _____

4. _____

5. _____

■ Step 5: Visualization and Healing Intentions

Now that you have a visual representation of your guilt and shame take a moment to visualize releasing these emotions from your life. Imagine each branch on your map gradually withering away, leaving space for new growth and healing.

Set an intention to work on healing these wounds as you move forward in your journey. Write down one or two practical steps you can take to address the root causes of your guilt and shame and how you will replace them with new, healthy habits that align with the life you deserve.

1. _____

_____

2. _____

_____

Why Self-Forgiveness is Critical in Shadow Work

Self-forgiveness is the cornerstone of profound healing and personal evolution. The beacon of light guides us through the maze of our inner world, illuminating the darkest corners of our consciousness. Here's why it's absolutely critical:

◆ **Release from emotional bonds:** Forgiving yourself is like breaking free from heavy chains that bind you to past mistakes and regrets. It releases the emotional burden holding you back, allowing you to soar toward personal growth.

- **Healing and transformation:** Self-forgiveness is the balm that soothes wounds you may not even be fully aware of. It's a potent elixir that promotes inner healing, allowing you to mend what's broken within and blossom into your fullest self.

- **Breaking cycles:** Shadow work is about breaking free from the recurring patterns that have kept you stuck in a loop of self-sabotage and pain. Self-forgiveness is the key to dismantling these cycles and forging a new path toward the life you truly deserve.

 ## Common Blocks to Self-Forgiveness

Before we embark on this journey, let's acknowledge the roadblocks that often hinder self-forgiveness:

- **Ingrained beliefs:** We may carry beliefs that tell us we don't deserve forgiveness, that we're unworthy of it. These beliefs can be deeply ingrained from childhood or past experiences.

- **Past experiences:** Traumatic experiences or past relationships can leave scars that make it challenging to forgive ourselves. We may blame ourselves for things beyond our control.

 ## The Role of Self-Forgiveness in Acknowledging and Accepting the Shadow Self

Self-forgiveness plays a pivotal role in shadow work because it encourages us to acknowledge and accept our shadow self without judgment. It is the bridge between our conscious and subconscious minds, fostering a sense of unity within ourselves.

Now, let's embark on a journey of self-discovery and healing with these journal prompts to get you started:

♦ What would change in my life if I truly forgave myself for past mistakes?

_____

_____

_____

_____

_____

♦ How would my relationships change if I let go of grudges and embraced forgiveness?

_____

_____

_____

_____

_____

♦ What do I need to accept about myself to be able to forgive others without judgment?

_____

_____

_____

_____

_____

♦ What are the benefits of forgiveness? How can I remind myself of these in times of forgiveness?

_____

_____

_____

_____

_____

◆ How can I show empathy and understanding when working through forgiveness for others?

_____

_____

_____

_____

_____

_____

Feel free to add your own prompts as well, tailored to your unique journey and experiences. Remember, you are not alone on this path; you have the strength and wisdom within you to navigate the depths of your subconscious and emerge stronger and more whole than ever before.

Exercise: Self-Forgiveness Letter

Begin by reflecting on your journey so far. Think about the past experiences, mistakes, and actions that have caused you guilt, shame, or self-blame. Recognize that these experiences are part of your past, and they do not define your worth or potential.

> **Start writing a letter of forgiveness to yourself. Address it as if you were writing to a dear friend who had experienced the same pain and suffering. Be honest, vulnerable, and compassionate as you express your forgiveness. Here are some prompts to guide your writing:**

♦ Begin by acknowledging that you are human and humans make mistakes. Embrace your imperfections as part of your unique journey.

♦ Describe the specific actions or events that you are forgiving yourself for. Don't hold back; let your emotions flow onto the paper.

♦ Say, "I forgive you," to yourself. Write why you are forgiving yourself and what you have learned from these experiences.

♦ Extend compassion and understanding to yourself. Write words of comfort and encouragement as if you were comforting a dear friend.

♦ Promise yourself that you are committed to healing and growth. Outline the steps you will take to prevent repeating the same patterns.

Dear Friend: _____,   Date:_____

_____

_____

_____

_____

_____

_____

_____

_____

_____

_____

_____

_____

_____

_____

_____

_____

_____

_____

_____

_____

_____

_____

_____

_____

_____

_____

_____

After writing your forgiveness letter, take some time to write about your experience. Here are some journal prompts to help you articulate your feelings and thoughts:

◆ Now that you have written this letter, what emotions surfaced? Did you experience any resistance or relief?

_____

_____

_____

_____

_____

_____

◆ Reflect on the specific actions or events you forgave yourself for. How have they impacted your life, relationships, or self-esteem?

_____

_____

_____

_____

_____

_____

◆ What have you learned from these experiences? How can you use this knowledge to make better choices in the future?

_____

_____

_____

_____

_____

◆ How will forgiving yourself help you break free from old cycles and create a healthier, more aligned life?

_____

_____

_____

_____

_____

◆ What steps will you take to ensure that you continue on your path of healing and growth?

1. _____

2. _____

3. _____

4. _____

5. _____

Remember, this process is about releasing the weight of the past and embracing your potential for a brighter future. You deserve love, compassion, and forgiveness just as much as anyone else. Keep this letter as a reminder of your commitment to self-compassion and healing.

The Guilt to Growth Transformation

Guilt is a complex emotion, often shrouded in negativity and self-blame. But, as you already know, our emotions are not inherently good or bad; they are valuable signals from our inner selves. Guilt, when harnessed and reframed correctly, can become an invaluable guide toward aligning your actions and behaviors with your true self, your values, and your aspirations.

So, let's delve into the essence of this transformation:

Understanding Guilt

To transform guilt, it's essential to explore its roots within your shadow self. Guilt often emerges when you believe you've violated your own values or moral code. It functions as an internal signal, drawing attention to areas in your life that may be influenced by your hidden, unacknowledged aspects. For example, if you've been neglecting your relationships due to work commitments and feel guilty about it, this guilt may signify that your shadow self values connection and that nurturing relationships align with your deeper desires and values.

 ## Reframing Guilt as a Guide

Instead of viewing guilt as punishment or a source of shame, reframe it as a guiding light. Imagine guilt as your inner compass, gently nudging you to explore aspects of your life that may be incongruent with your true self. For example, if you feel guilty about not pursuing your passion for painting, consider it a signal to explore this creative side of yourself, aligning with your genuine interests.

 ## Guilt as Fuel for Change

Guilt can be a powerful motivator. Embrace it as a constructive force that propels you toward positive transformation. When guilt arises, ask yourself, "What can I learn from this? How can I grow?" For instance, if you feel guilty about neglecting your physical health, use that guilt to motivate yourself to adopt healthier habits, such as regular exercise and balanced nutrition. Channel this energy into actionable steps that align with your values and intentions.

 ## Shadow Integration

This workbook encourages you to explore your shadow self more deeply. Guilt often originates from unacknowledged aspects of your shadow, those hidden facets of your personality you may have suppressed or denied. Shadow integration is a vital part of this journey, as it helps you reconcile with these hidden parts of yourself. An example might be realizing that your guilt about speaking up in social situations is tied to a hidden fear of rejection. By integrating this fear into your conscious awareness, you can work on overcoming it and become more confident in social interactions.

 Creating Healthy Habits

Ultimately, this transformation goes beyond healing; it's about creating that life that aligns with who you are. You'll learn how to replace old, self-limiting habits with new, healthy ones that support your journey toward the life you genuinely deserve. For instance, if you've been using excessive screen time as a coping mechanism for emotional pain, you'll develop new habits like mindfulness practices or seeking support from loved ones instead.

 Journal Prompts: Shame Release

Shame has a profound impact on our self-image, behavior, and overall well-being. In order to break free from destructive cycles and create a life that aligns with your true self, it's essential to confront and heal the wounds of shame.

 These journal prompts are designed to guide you through the process of releasing shame. They will encourage deep reflection, self-compassion, and self-awareness. Remember, this work may be challenging, but it's also incredibly liberating. You are taking a courageous step toward lasting healing and growth.

Think back to a specific moment in your life when you felt intense shame. Describe the situation, your emotions, and any physical sensations that accompanied it. How did this experience shape your self-image at the time?

_____

_____

_____

_____

_____

Reflect on the impact of shame on your relationships. Have there been times when you withheld your true self or felt disconnected from others because of shame? How has shame influenced your ability to connect authentically with others?

_____

_____

_____

_____

_____

Explore the coping mechanisms you've developed to deal with shame. Have they been healthy or harmful? How have these strategies affected your overall well-being and the way you handle shame in the present?

_____

_____

_____

_____

_____

Identify any recurring patterns or triggers that bring up feelings of shame in your life. What do these patterns reveal about your core wounds? How can you respond to these triggers with self-compassion and understanding?

_____

_____

_____

_____

_____

Envision a future where shame no longer holds power over you. What does that life look like? How do you want to feel about yourself and your relationships? What steps can you take to move toward this liberated state?

_____

_____

_____

_____

_____

As you work through these journal prompts, remember that healing from shame is a journey, not a destination. Be patient with yourself and honor the courage it takes to face these challenging emotions. By confronting your shame, you're creating the space for deep healing and personal transformation.

 ## Affirmations

 These affirmations are tools to help you release guilt and shame, allowing you to embrace self-forgiveness and emotional mastery. Repeat them daily, and watch as they gradually transform your inner world:

♦ *I am worthy of love and forgiveness, just as I am.* This affirmation reminds you that your past does not define your worth. You are deserving of love and forgiveness simply because you exist.

♦ *I release the weight of guilt and shame from my heart.* Visualize the burden of guilt and shame lifting from your chest as you say this affirmation. Let go of what no longer serves you.

- *I am not defined by my past; I am creating my future.* Your past does not dictate your future. You have the power to shape the life you want, free from the constraints of guilt and shame.

- *I forgive myself for any mistakes I've made, knowing they were lessons for growth.* Forgiving yourself is a powerful act of self-compassion.

- *I am in control of my emotions; they do not control me.* You have the ability to master your emotions rather than letting them control you. This affirmation reinforces your emotional strength.

- *I release the need for external validation; I validate myself.* Rely on your own validation rather than seeking it from others. This affirmation promotes self-acceptance and confidence.

- *I am resilient, and I have proven that I can overcome any challenge put in my path.* Believe in your resilience and inner strength. You have the capacity to overcome any obstacle on your healing journey.

- *I embrace my shadows with love and acceptance.* Acknowledge and accept all parts of yourself, even the ones you've tried to hide. Lovingly integrate them into your whole being.

- *I trust in the process of healing; I am unfolding into my highest self.* Trust that your journey of self-discovery and healing is leading you toward becoming the best version of yourself.

- *I am the author of my life story, and I choose to write a story filled with love and joy.*

You have the power to shape your life's narrative. Choose to write a story that reflects the love and joy you deserve. Remember, the path of deep subconscious exploration and emotional mastery is not always easy, but it is profoundly rewarding. These affirmations are your daily companions, helping you break free from old patterns and embrace a life filled with healing and growth.

In the preceding chapter, we've ventured into the profound territory of our hidden depths, confronting the often elusive emotions of shame and guilt. We've learned that these feelings, though uncomfortable, are powerful messengers from our inner world, urging us to explore uncharted territories of our psyche. By understanding their origins and embracing them as catalysts for change, we've begun the journey of self-forgiveness and personal growth.

Now, as we turn the page toward our final chapter, we step into the light of self-acceptance and integration. The path ahead is one of harmony with our shadow self, recognizing that every facet of our being has a purpose and a place in the tapestry of our existence.

In the pages that follow, we'll delve deeper into practical steps and daily habits that will empower you to live authentically, honoring your entire being. These habits will guide you in your ongoing journey toward emotional mastery and self-discovery. With each new day, you'll find yourself more aligned with your true self, living a life that reflects the wisdom and power of your enlightened shadow.

CHAPTER 8
THE ENLIGHTMENT SHADOW

The Enlightment Shadow

> **"**
>
> *One does not become enlightened by imagining figures of light, but by making the darkness conscious. –Carl Jung*
>
> **"**

This chapter represents the culmination of your efforts, the moment when you step into the light and embrace the enlightened shadow within you. It's a place where healing meets growth, self-acceptance becomes self-love, and you truly begin to live in harmony with your entire being.

It's not just about understanding your past wounds; it's about using that knowledge to forge a brighter future. It's about rising above the cycles that once held you captive and creating new, healthy habits that align with the life you truly deserve. This is the chapter where you'll learn how to integrate your newfound wisdom into your daily life and let it shine as a beacon of your inner strength.

Understanding Shadow Integration

In the beginner's guide to shadow work, you were introduced to the fundamental concept of shadow integration. Now, we will expand upon those foundations with advanced knowledge to help you gain a deeper understanding and achieve lasting emotional mastery.

To truly master your shadow, it's essential to live in harmony with every facet of yourself, even the parts you may have tried to bury or ignore. Recognizing and accepting all aspects of your being is the key to emotional liberation. It's not about suppressing your shadows; it's about embracing them.

Embracing who you truly are can bring profound peace and serenity to your life.

How to accept yourself:

- **Forgive yourself:** Understand that you are not defined by your past mistakes. Forgiving yourself is an act of self-compassion that opens the door to healing.

- **Use present moment awareness and mindfulness:** Stay grounded in the present, acknowledging your feelings without judgment. This empowers you to respond consciously rather than reactively.

- **Acknowledge and love your abilities:** Celebrate your strengths and talents. They are a part of your unique self.

- **Ignore your inner critic:** Challenge your self-critical thoughts and replace them with self-affirming ones.

- **Connect with loved ones who appreciate you:** Surround yourself with people who support and love you for who you are.

- **Move on from disappointments:** Release the grip of past disappointments, as they do not define your worth or potential.

◆ **Gain perspective on your limitations:** Recognize that limitations are not weaknesses but opportunities for growth.

The Influence of Caregivers and Life Experiences

From the moment of our birth, the influence of caregivers and life circumstances shapes our self-perception. Understanding this influence is key as we continue on the journey of self-acceptance and shadow integration. Whether your upbringing was marked by love and acceptance or challenges, it has contributed to who you are today.

Shadow Integration: The True Path to Personal Growth

It's important to clarify that the shadow is not the source of evil, prejudice, or hate. Instead, our failure to recognize and integrate the shadow creates these negative influences. By acknowledging and embracing our inner darkness, we can evolve individually and as a society.

Shadow work is a key step in growth and self-discovery. Without integrating the shadow, it continues to affect our behavior and experiences. To become your highest self, you must accept the entirety of your being, including your darkest aspects. Your shadow self is a part of you, but it does not get to decide who you are.

Journaling is an invaluable tool for deep self-discovery and shadow work. It allows you to explore and document every facet of your journey, no matter how small or significant. Pay close attention to your reactions as you uncover hidden parts of yourself, as this is where your shadow often manifests most prominently.

Your shadow self often reveals itself in your immediate reactions to stressful situations or unfamiliar environments. Train yourself to slow down and observe these knee-jerk responses. This process requires time and self-compassion but leads to profound self-understanding.

When you encounter aspects of your shadow self, resist the urge to doubt or rationalize them away. Trust your instincts and the insights that arise during your shadow work. If your shadow self were rational, it wouldn't be something you needed to address.

Finally, remember that shadow work is not a one-time endeavor. It's a lifelong process of growth and self-discovery. Embrace the fact that there will always be more to explore and heal. This ongoing journey is a testament to your commitment to becoming the best version of yourself.

As you travel this advanced exploration of your shadow, remember that you have the strength and resilience to face any challenge. The path ahead may be challenging, but it is also deeply rewarding. You are on the road to a life filled with healing, growth, and the fulfillment you truly deserve.

 ## *Reflective Questions for Self-Discovery*

 This exercise is designed to help you uncover your feelings and thoughts about your shadow aspects. Remember, this is an advanced workbook, and the questions are meant to dig deep and support your journey toward healing and growth. Take your time with each question, and be honest and compassionate with yourself as you explore your inner world.

What recurring patterns or behaviors do you notice in your life that you believe might be connected to your shadow aspects? Take some time to think about specific situations or behaviors that have been consistent over time. These could be in relationships, careers, or personal habits.

_____

_____

_____

_____

_____

_____

Can you identify any childhood memories or experiences that may have contributed to the development of these patterns or behaviors? Sometimes, our shadow aspects have their roots in our early experiences. Reflect on any significant moments from your past that could be influencing your present.

_____

_____

_____

_____

_____

_____

How do these patterns or behaviors make you feel about yourself? Explore your emotions associated with these patterns. Do they make you feel inadequate, anxious, angry, or something else entirely?

_____

_____

_____

_____

_____

_____

What are the stories or beliefs you tell yourself about these patterns? Often, our shadow aspects are accompanied by negative self-talk or limiting beliefs. Try to pinpoint the stories you tell yourself in relation to these patterns.

_____

_____

_____

_____

Have you ever tried to suppress or ignore these aspects of yourself? If so, why? Consider whether you've consciously or unconsciously tried to avoid confronting your shadow aspects and the reasons behind them.

_____

_____

_____

_____

_____

How have these patterns affected your relationships, both with yourself and with others? Explore how your shadow aspects have influenced your interactions with others and your self-esteem.

_____

_____

_____

_____

_____

What would it mean to you to fully embrace and integrate these shadow aspects into your life? Imagine a scenario where you fully accept and work with these aspects of yourself. How would your life change? How would you feel?

_____

_____

_____

_____

_____

Are there any fears or resistance you have about facing these shadow aspects head-on? Often, there's a fear of the unknown or of potential discomfort associated with diving deep into our shadows. Identify any such fears.

_____

_____

_____

_____

_____

Can you recall any moments in your life when you experienced a breakthrough or insight related to your shadow aspects? What led to that realization? Sometimes, past breakthroughs can provide clues about how to approach your current journey of self-discovery.

_____

_____

_____

_____

_____

What are some practical steps you can take to begin addressing and healing these shadow aspects? Start brainstorming actionable steps you can implement to start the healing and transformation process.

1. _____

2. _____

3. _____

4. _____

5. _____

 ## *Daily Practices for Self-Discovery*

 Daily practices for shadow integration can be a powerful way to increase self-awareness, personal growth, and emotional healing. Here are some daily habits to promote mindfulness and self-reflection, helping you regularly acknowledge and integrate your shadow self:

Daily Mindfulness Habits

- **Morning meditation:** Start your day with a short meditation session to center yourself and become aware of your thoughts and feelings.

- **Mindful breathing:** Throughout the day, take short breaks to focus on your breath. The intention is to stay present and be mindful of your thoughts without judgment.

- **Mindful eating:** What does it taste like? Be mindful of the texture and smell of your food during meals. Mindful eating can bring awareness to your relationship with nourishment.

- **Body scan:** Dedicate a few minutes each day to a body scan, where you focus on different parts of your body and notice any tension or discomfort.

- **Journaling:** Write in a journal to express your thoughts and feelings. Reflect on your experiences and emotions without censoring yourself.

Daily Self-Reflection

- **Daily gratitude practice:** Each day, write down three things you're grateful for. This encourages a positive outlook and self-awareness.

- **Emotion check-in:** Take a moment to identify your current emotions and explore the underlying reasons for them.

- **Review your day:** Before bed, review your day and any significant interactions or events. Consider how your shadow self may have influenced your actions.

Daily Shadow Integration in 4 Steps

- **Choose a shadow to integrate:** Each day, consciously select a shadow aspect or negative trait you'd like to explore and integrate.

- **Face the shadow with two-way attention:** Spend some time in introspection, examining the chosen shadow without judgment. Acknowledge its presence within you.

- **Interrogate the shadow:** Ask questions to understand the shadow better. Start by addressing it in the third person (e.g., "What does it want?"), then shift to second person (e.g., "What do you want?"). This helps you see it from different perspectives.

♦ **Own the shadow and forgive:** Embrace the shadow as a part of yourself, showing self-compassion and understanding. Forgive yourself for any past actions or thoughts associated with this shadow. Let it go with love and acceptance.

 ## *Exercise: The Daily Shadow Log*

Every day, you will use one of these log sheets to record and reflect on your interactions with your shadow. The shadow represents the hidden, often unconscious, aspects of your personality, including your fears, insecurities, and suppressed emotions. By bringing these aspects into the light, you can turn them from detractors into sources of strength. If you need to print out additional daily logs, they are available at AdvancedShadow.LeighWHart.com

Write down the date at the beginning of each journal entry. This will help you track your progress over time.

Date:_____

Morning Reflection:

♦ Start your day by setting an intention to explore your shadow. Write down what emotions or situations do you anticipate encountering today that may trigger your shadow?

_____

_____

_____

_____

Daily Interactions:

Throughout the day, take note of any moments when your shadow emerges. These may be situations where you feel anger, fear, jealousy, insecurity, or any other challenging emotion. Be honest and detailed in your descriptions.

◆ **Time:** Record the time of the interaction.

_____

◆ **Situation/Trigger:** Describe the event or situation that triggered your shadow.

_____

_____

_____

_____

_____

◆ **Emotions:** List the emotions you experienced during this interaction.

1. _____

2. _____

3. _____

◆ **Thoughts:** Write down any negative or self-critical thoughts that arose.

1. _____

2. _____

3. _____

- **Reactions:** Describe how you reacted or responded to the situation.

_____

_____

_____

_____

_____

- **Physical Sensations:** Note any physical sensations, such as tension or discomfort.

1. _____

2. _____

3. _____

Evening Reflection:

- Review your daily interactions and observations in the evening.

- Identify any recurring patterns or themes in your shadow interactions.

1. _____

2. _____

3. _____

- Reflect on how these patterns may be linked to past experiences or beliefs

Embracing Your Shadow:

Understanding your shadow is the first step in transforming it from a hidden detractor into a source of strength. Here are some tips to help you embrace your shadow:

- **Self-Compassion:** Be gentle with yourself. Your shadow contains aspects of yourself you've likely been avoiding or suppressing for a long time. Treat these parts of yourself with kindness and empathy.

- **Awareness:** The more aware you become of your shadow, the better equipped you'll be to work with it. Keep using this journal to shine a light on your hidden aspects.

- **Acceptance:** Accept that owning your shadow is a natural part of you, and that is human. It doesn't make you flawed or broken; it makes you whole.

- **Integration:** Gradually integrate the lessons and education you gained from your shadow work with your daily life. Use what you discover to make healthier choices and build new, empowering habits.

 ## *A Story of Transformation*

In a small, close-knit community, there lived a woman named Sarah, who was known for her warmth and kindness. But beneath her friendly exterior lay a deep-seated fear of rejection that had plagued her for years. She had always been the one to offer support and comfort to others, yet she struggled to reveal her own vulnerabilities.

One day, Sarah met Mark, a man who had his own demons to face. Mark had always grappled with anger issues that seemed to erupt at the slightest provocation. It had cost him relationships, opportunities, and inner peace. But he was determined to change, to find a way to transform his anger into something constructive.

As fate would have it, Sarah and Mark crossed paths and found solace in each other's presence. Sarah's fear of rejection and Mark's anger were like mirror images of each other. They decided to embark on a journey of self-discovery together, supporting one another through their respective challenges.

They met regularly to share their experiences, fears, and triumphs. Sarah, inspired by Mark's determination, decided to confront her fear of rejection head-on. She began by opening up to Mark about her insecurities, allowing herself to be vulnerable in a way she never had before. Mark, in turn, shared his strategies for managing anger and finding inner peace.

Their friendship blossomed as they continued to work on themselves. Sarah found that by embracing vulnerability, she not only deepened her connection with Mark but also transformed her relationships with others. She learned that true strength lay in authenticity and that her fear of rejection no longer held her captive.

Mark, too, made significant progress on his journey. By acknowledging his anger issues and seeking healthy outlets for his emotions, he not only improved his relationships but also discovered a newfound sense of inner peace. His anger became a catalyst for personal growth rather than a destructive force.

As Sarah and Mark's stories intertwined, they encountered Maria, a woman who had spent most of her life struggling with self-doubt and a crippling lack of self-worth. Her childhood wounds had left scars that she had tried to hide for years.

Seeing the transformation in Sarah and Mark, Maria felt inspired to confront her own demons. She joined their support group, sharing her experiences and fears. With the guidance and encouragement of her newfound friends, Maria began the difficult journey of working through her childhood wounds, one painful memory at a time.

As Sarah, Mark, and Maria continued to support each other, they discovered that by acknowledging their darker aspects, they not only found healing but also unlocked their true potential. Their shared experiences taught them that embracing vulnerability, managing anger, and working through deep-seated wounds were powerful tools for personal growth and self-discovery.

Together, they proved that the path to a richer, more authentic life was not without its challenges, but it was a journey worth taking. Through their courage and determination, they transformed their lives and became beacons of hope for others seeking to confront their shadows and find the light within.

In the end, Sarah, Mark, and Maria's intertwined stories served as a testament to the profound change that could occur when one dared to acknowledge their darker aspects and turn them into sources of strength and authenticity. Their journey was a powerful reminder that healing and growth were within reach for anyone willing to take that courageous step into the depths of their own psyche.

Sustaining Growth and Balancing the Self

It's time to discuss how to sustain your growth and maintain a balanced self through the ongoing practice of shadow work.

Integrating Shadow Work into Everyday Life

Shadow work isn't a one-time endeavor; it's a lifelong commitment to self-awareness and growth. To keep making progress, consider these strategies:

- **Daily reflection:** Dedicate a few moments each day to reflect on your emotions, thoughts, and behaviors. Journaling can be immensely helpful in this regard. Write down your observations, insights, and any triggers that come up.

- **Mindfulness practice:** Incorporate mindfulness techniques into your daily routine. This will help you stay present and aware of your emotions as they arise. When you catch yourself reacting from a place of unconscious patterns, pause and breathe.

- **Regular check-ins:** Set aside time every week or month for a deeper dive into your shadow. Schedule sessions with a therapist or coach to help you navigate and process what you uncover.

- **Accountability partner:** Find a trusted friend or partner who is also committed to personal growth. Share your experiences and insights, and support each other in staying on track.

Self-Compassion and Patience

Remember that shadow work can be challenging, and it's okay to take things at your own pace. Here's how to embrace self-compassion and patience in this lifelong process:

- **Be kind to yourself:** Understand that healing deep-seated wounds takes time. Instead of harsh self-judgment, treat yourself with the same kindness and empathy you would offer a dear friend.

- **Embrace setbacks:** Expect that you may encounter setbacks along the way. See them as opportunities to learn and grow. Every stumble is a chance to refine your understanding of yourself.

- **Celebrate:** Your achievements deserve to be acknowledged and celebrated. Each step you take toward self-awareness and emotional mastery is a victory.

- **Seek support:** Don't hesitate to lean on your support network when times get tough. Whether it's friends or family, reaching out for help is a sign of strength, not weakness.

Remember, the journey of shadow work is not about perfection; it's about progress. By integrating shadow work into your daily life and nurturing self-compassion and patience, you'll find the resilience and inner balance needed to face your deepest wounds and create lasting change.

You're on the path to a life that aligns with your true self and the growth you deserve. Keep moving forward with confidence and determination.

 ## *Growth Milestone Tracker*

 As you embark on this transformative journey, I want to provide you with a tool that will help you track and celebrate your personal growth achievements. The Growth Milestone Tracker is designed to be your compass, guiding you through the intricate terrain of your inner world as you work on healing and breaking free from old cycles.

Setting Your Intentions: Before you begin, take a moment to reflect on your intentions for this journey. What specific areas of your life do you want to transform? What patterns and wounds are you ready to face and heal? Write down your intentions in the space provided.

```
┌──────────────────────────────────────────────────────┐
│        My intentions for this journey:                │
│                                                        │
│   _____    │
│   _____    │
│   _____    │
│   _____    │
│                                                        │
└──────────────────────────────────────────────────────┘
```

Identifying key milestones: In the space provided, list the key milestones or goals you hope to achieve through your shadow work. These milestones should be specific, actionable, and related to the healing and growth you seek. For example, "Confront and heal childhood trauma," "Develop healthier communication patterns," or "Release self-sabotaging beliefs.

```
┌──────────────────────────────────────────────────────┐
│                "My Key Milestones:"                   │
│                                                        │
│   1. _____  │
│   2. _____  │
│   3. _____  │
│   4. _____  │
│   5. _____  │
│                                                        │
└──────────────────────────────────────────────────────┘
```

Recording your progress: As you work through this workbook, periodically revisit your Growth Milestone Tracker. For each milestone you achieve or make significant progress toward, record the date and a brief note on your progress in the respective columns.

Milestone	Date Achieved	Progress Note
1.		
2.		
3.		
4.		
5.		
6.		
7.		
8.		
9.		
10.		

Celebrating your achievements: Celebrate each milestone as it comes. Acknowledge the effort and courage it took to get there. You can celebrate in your own unique way, whether it's treating yourself to something special, journaling about your success, or simply sharing your accomplishment with someone you trust.

Staying committed: Remember, this journey is about deep healing and lasting transformation. There may be moments of discomfort and resistance, but those are signs of growth. Use this tracker as a reminder of your commitment to yourself and your desire for a more fulfilling life.

Revising and adding milestones: As you progress, you may find that new milestones emerge or that your initial goals need adjustment. Feel free to revise and add to your list as your understanding deepens and your journey evolves.

Your Growth Milestone Tracker is a tangible testament to your commitment to healing and growth. Each milestone reached represents a step closer to the life you truly deserve. Be patient with yourself, embrace the challenges, and know that you are on a path toward profound transformation.

You've taken the advanced step of delving deeper into your shadows, and with each milestone achieved, you are reclaiming your power and rewriting your narrative. Trust the process, and know that you have the inner strength to overcome whatever obstacles may arise.

Affirmations

Let's create a set of powerful affirmations for your advanced shadow work workbook. These affirmations will help you dive deeper into your subconscious, master your emotions, and reframe your cognition for lasting healing and growth.

I encourage you to repeat these affirmations daily and to truly believe in their potential for transformation:

- *"I am courageous and ready to face my inner shadows with love and compassion."*
- *"I embrace discomfort as an opportunity for profound growth and self-discovery."*
- *"I release the past and its hold on me, making room for a brighter future."*
- *"I trust in my ability to heal and transform, one step at a time."*
- *"I am worthy of love, acceptance, and all the blessings life has to offer."*
- *"I acknowledge my inner wounds without judgment, knowing that they are part of my journey."*

- "I choose to let go of self-limiting beliefs and replace them with empowering thoughts."

- "I am the author of my own narrative, and I am rewriting it with love and resilience."

- "I invite healing and positive change into my life by nurturing my inner self."

- "I am in control of my emotions, and I choose to respond with wisdom and grace."

- "I release the need for external validation and find validation within myself."

- "I am constantly evolving, and every challenge is an opportunity for growth."

- "I trust the process of life and surrender to the flow of healing and transformation."

- "I am a beacon of light, illuminating the darkest corners of my psyche with self-love."

- "I deserve a life filled with joy, purpose, and abundance, and I am taking steps to create it."

- "I am open to receiving support and guidance from within and from those who genuinely care about my well-being."

- "I am resilient, and I bounce back stronger from every setback."

- "I am the master of my thoughts, and I choose positivity and self-compassion."

- "I radiate love, and it attracts love and positivity into my life."

- "I am committed to my ongoing journey of self-discovery and growth, knowing that I am becoming the best version of myself."

In embracing our shadow self and integrating its lessons, we embark on a profound journey toward living in harmony with our true selves. Through the exploration of our hidden depths, we discover the invaluable gifts that lie within the shadows: wisdom, strength, and resilience. As we acknowledge and accept our darker aspects, we free ourselves from the confines of self-judgment and fear. Living in harmony with our shadow self is not about erasing darkness but about dancing with it, recognizing that it is an integral part of the whole. In this sacred dance, we find balance and authenticity, transforming our lives into a beautiful symphony of self-love, self-acceptance, and continuous growth. Embrace your shadow, for in doing so, you unlock the door to your fullest potential and the profound peace that comes from living in unity with your complete self.

Unveiling The Shadows: A Call To Share Your Journey

In the realm of shadow work, solidarity and understanding are invaluable treasures. When you leave a review, you send an echo of support into the void, letting others know that their struggles and victories are acknowledged and shared. This sense of community is vital in a journey that can often feel isolating.

So, I call upon you, brave navigators of the inner self, to share your journey, to leave a review for this advanced shadow work journal and workbook. Let your voice be heard, your journey acknowledged, and your wisdom shared. In doing so, you not only affirm your growth and transformation but also extend a hand to those still navigating their way through the shadows.

Sharing your challenges and triumphs can inspire others to take the first step, pick up this workbook, and confront their shadows with hope and determination.

YOU CAN HELP OTHERS!

Thank you so much for your support. We all need a helping hand from time to time and your words could be the spark that ignites someone's transformation.

Scan the QR code to leave a quick review.

Conclusion

As you reach the final pages of this advanced workbook for shadow integration, I want to commend you for embarking on this profound journey of self-discovery and healing. You've come a long way from the initial steps of exploring your shadow, and you've shown incredible resilience and determination to delve deeper into your subconscious, master your emotions, and reframe your cognition. This book has been your guide, offering you insights and tools to confront your inner shadows and transform them into allies on your path to a more fulfilling life.

Throughout these pages, we've touched upon essential topics crucial for your ongoing growth and self-empowerment. We've delved into the recesses of your mind to understand the roots of your feelings and emotions. We've unearthed the traumas, the wounded inner child, and the negative thought patterns that have shaped your existence, often in ways you may not have fully recognized until now.

We've explored the transformative power of turning hurt into healing and how this transformation can have a profound impact on your relationships, both with yourself and with others. You've learned how fear, anxiety, and depression can be harnessed as sources of strength, propelling you forward rather than holding you back. And you've bravely faced the daunting specters of shame and guilt, understanding that they too can be released, allowing you to step into the light of self-acceptance.

In the beginning, we introduced you to Christine, a woman who, like you, carried her childhood trauma and her shadow self as a heavy burden for most of her life. But her story serves as a beacon of hope and inspiration. Her courage to open those dark doors, confront her shadow, and integrate it into her being has transformed her existence. Today, at 52 years old, she shares her story to help others, proving that it's never too late to start this transformative work.

Remember, you are seen, valued, loved, and, most importantly, worth every ounce of effort you've put into this journey. Christine's story and the stories of countless others are testaments to the incredible resilience of the human spirit. You are no exception.

As you move forward, keep in mind that shadow integration is not a one-time endeavor but a lifelong practice. Continue to explore, embrace, and nurture your shadow self as a welcomed and cherished part of who you are. Your commitment to this work will lead you to a lifetime of joy and happiness.

I want to personally thank you for trusting in this process, for pushing your own boundaries, and for taking the courageous steps necessary to reclaim your life. I am genuinely proud of you, and I admire your unwavering dedication to your own growth and well-being.

With admiration,

Leigh W. Hart

Other Books You'll Love By
Leigh W Hart

Don't Get Derailed By Your Attachment Style

Whether you are anxious, avoidant, or fearful in relationships, this book will provide you with proven strategies for effectively dealing with an insecure attachment style.

Reparenting Your Wounded Inner Child

Explore Childhood and Generational Trauma to Break Destructive Patterns, Build Emotional Strength and Achieve Personal Growth with 7 Empowering Steps. Free yourself from the pains of the past and create a life you will love now and in the future.

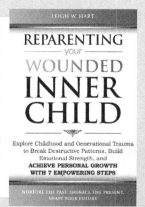

CBT Inner Child Workbook

Available Fall 2024

Heal Past Trauma, Restore Emotional Resilience, and Reclaim Your Joy with Cognitive Behavioral Therapy Exercises, Journal Prompts, and Self-love Practices. This workbook is your companion on the journey to nurture and heal your inner child.

Amazon.com/Author/LeighWHart

Elevate Your Journey...

with BONUS
Complimentary Support Materials

GIFT #1: Self-Assessment Tests, Printable Affirmations & Bonus Materials

As you begin your shadow work journey, are you unsure where to focus your efforts? Use the self-assessment tests to determine which areas of your life need the most attention.

GIFT #2: The Self-Discovery Workbook

Personal growth is a lifelong journey. Use this workbook now and in the future to revisit insights learned, reevaluate your progress, and continue evolving on your path to personal fulfillment.

GIFT #3: The Evolving Growth Workbook

Personal growth is a lifelong journey. Use this workbook now and in the future to revisit insights learned, reevaluate your progress, and continue evolving on your path to personal fulfillment.

Go to:
Shadow.LeighWHart.com
to receive your BONUS printable support materials.

My GIFT to you!

References

Ackerman, C. (2018, July 12). What is self-acceptance? 25 exercises + definition and quotes. PositivePsychology.com. https://positivepsychology.com/self-acceptance/

Aletheia. (2023, July 8). 7 inner archetypes that cripple your confidence and self-respect. LonerWolf. https://lonerwolf.com/inner-archetype-examples/

Andrews, W. (2020, September 13). Find your true self by overcoming fears. Design.org. https://design.org/find-your-true-self-by-overcoming-fears/

Applegate, D. (2023, March 1). How to identify, heal, & integrate your emotional triggers. Rediscovering Sacredness | Dominica Applegate. https://rediscoveringsacredness.com/how-to-identify-heal-integrate-your-emotional-triggers/

Cherry, K. (2023, February 27). The structure and levels of the mind according to Freud. Verywell Mind. https://www.verywellmind.com/the-conscious-and-unconscious-mind-2795946#:~:text=According%20to%20Freud%2C%20thoughts%20and

Crady, A. (2022, October 14). How doing shadow work for 10 months has seriously improved my life. Ascent Publication. https://medium.com/the-ascent/how-doing-shadow-work-for-10-months-has-seriously-improved-my-life-c1cae10b6dd6

Creating a healing space at home with these 5 steps. (2021, January 12). Healing Works Foundation. https://healingworksfoundation.org/5-ways-to-make-your-home-a-healing-space/

Eanes, R. (n.d.). Accepting ourselves and our children while embracing growth and change. Genmindful.com. https://genmindful.com/blogs/mindful-moments/accepting-ourselves-and-our-children-while-embracing-growth-and-change

Edwards, W. (2021). 7 inner child archetypes. Simple and Deep. https://www.wysteriaedwards.com/blog/7%20Inner%20Child%20Archetypes

Emotion exploration scale (worksheet). (2022, May 2). Therapist Aid. https://www.therapistaid.com/therapy-worksheet/emotion-exploration-scale

Erasmus, Y. (2021, February 23). Learning the art of emotional alchemy. Yvetteerasmus.com. https://yvetteerasmus.com/feelings/learning-the-art-of-emotional-alchemy/

5 ways to challenge negative thoughts. (2021, February 11). Eugene Therapy. https://eugenetherapy.com/article/5-ways-to-challenge-negative-thoughts/

Fritscher, L. (2023, May 17). How Carl Jung's collective unconscious is tied to dreams, beliefs, and phobias. Verywell Mind. https://www.verywellmind.com/what-is-the-collective-unconscious-2671571#:~:text=Ongoing%20Research-

Fuller, K. (2020, July 14). 5 elements of shadow work you must incorporate to become your highest self. ILLUMINATION. https://medium.com/illumination/5-elements-of-shadow-work-you-must-incorporate-to-become-your-highest-self-6f3d35205291

Goldstein, A. (2018, January 19). Integrating shadow work® and mindfulness. Shadowwork.com. https://shadow-work.com/integrating-shadow-work-mindfulness/

Helen Keller quotes. (n.d.). BrainyQuote. Retrieved December 5, 2023, from https://www.brainyquote.com/quotes/helen_keller_109208

J, E. (2023, October 8). How to practice mindfulness with shadow work. Medium. https://medium.com/@reading-witheash/how-to-practice-mindfulness-with-shadow-work-565ae3a07813

Kashtan, I., & Kashtan, M. (n.d.). Basics of nonviolent communication. Bay NVC. https://baynvc.org/basics-of-non-violent-communication/#:~:text=Both%20are%20ex-pressed%20through%20four

Kate. (2023, June 22). Attachment theory: Attraction is subconscious | healthy wealthy lifestyles. THE SMRT LIST. https://24caratinc.io/attachment-theory-attrac-tion-is-subconscious/

Khoddam, R. (2021, March 3). How trauma affects the body. Psychology Today. https://www.psychologytoday.com/ca/blog/the-addiction-connection/202103/how-trauma-affects-the-body

Kress, D. A. (2019, February 5). Healing your relationship to your ego. Dr. Anna Kress. https://drannakress.com/healing-your-relationship-to-your-ego/#:~:text=The%20Ego%20as%20a%20Trauma

Kristenson, S. (2022, January 16). How to reparent yourself: A 7-step guide. Happier Human. https://www.happierhuman.com/reparent-yourself/

Lovering, N. (2019, October 7). 8 ways to channel your anger productively. Psych Central. https://psychcentral.com/blog/how-to-channel-your-anger-into-productive-action#tips

Lucie, N. (2023, January 7). Healing hidden trauma with the help of shadow work. The Feminine Principle. https://thefeminineprinciple.com/healing-hidden-trauma-with-the-help-of-shadow-work#:~:text=As%20a%20re-sult%2C%20what%20we

Mahatma Gandhi quotes. (2023, December 7). BrainyQuote. https://www.brainyquote.com/quotes/mahatma_gand-hi_125863

Mahoney, M. (2003, January 13). The subconscious mind of the consumer (and how to reach it). HBS Working Knowl-edge. https://hbswk.hbs.edu/item/the-subconscious-mind-of-the-consumer-and-how-to-reach-it

Marteka. (2019, July 15). 12 ways to recognise negative thoughts. Benevolent Health. https://benevolenthealth. co.uk/12-ways-to-recognise-negative-thoughts/

Metivier, A. (2022, May 4). Magnetic memory method - memory improvement made easy with Anthony Metivier. Magnetic Memory Method - How to Memorize with a Memory Palace. https://www.magneticmemorymethod. com/subconscious-mind-exercises/

Mindfulness STOP skill. (2023, December 1). Cognitive Behavioral Therapy Los Angeles. https://cogbtherapy.com/ mindfulness-meditation-blog/mindfulness-stop-skill

Oppong, T. (2023, April 22). Freedom is what you do with what's been done to you. Mind Cafe. https://medium. com/mind-cafe/freedom-is-what-you-do-with-whats-been-done-to-you-jean-paul-sartre-d8645e0da5fc

Prana, T. (2020, February 25). 30 affirmations to reprogram my subconscious mind. Www.linkedin.com. https://www. linkedin.com/pulse/30-affirmations-reprogram-my-subconscious-mind-trias-prananingrum/

A quote by C.G. Jung. (n.d.). Www.goodreads.com. Retrieved December 3, 2023, from https://www.goodreads.com/ quotes/44379-until-you-make-the-unconsciousconscious-it-will-direct-your

A quote by Paul Boese. (n.d.). Goodreads. Retrieved December 10, 2023, from https://www.goodreads.com/ quotes/6603442-forgiveness-does-not-change-the-past-but-it-does-enlarge

Ralph Waldo Emerson Quotes. (n.d.). Www.forbes.com. Retrieved December 11, 2023, from https://www.forbes. com/quotes/author/ralph-waldo-emerson/

Rickardsson, J. (2023, July 1). 5 Reasons why empathy is important in relationships. 29k. https://29k.org/article/5-reasons-why-empathy-is-important-in-relationships

Ridsdel, J. (2021, April 1). 10 common negative thinking patterns and 5 steps for change. Www.familycentre.org. https://www.familycentre.org/news/post/10-common-negative-thinking-patterns-and-5-steps-for-change

Roselle. (2018, November 4). 5 Signs of emotional intensity and why you're awesome. Roselle Caballes. https://rosel-lecaballes.com/blog/emotional-intensity-5-signs-that-youre-an-emotionally-intense-person-and-why-youre-awesome

7 advanced techniques to experience deep meditation. (2023, November 27). Calm Blog. https://www.calm.com/blog/deep-meditation

Siegel-Acevedo, D. (2021, July 1). Writing can help us heal from trauma. Harvard Business Review. https://hbr.org/2021/07/writing-can-help-us-heal-from-trauma

6 subconscious journaling techniques. (2020, September 21). Inspired Meditations. https://www.inspiredmeditations.com/6-subconscious-journaling-techniques/

Types of trauma. (2023, October 26). The Trauma Practice. https://traumapractice.co.uk/types-of-trauma/

Walsh, K. (2023, March 20). 5 ways to reparent your inner child and heal from old wounds. https://www.dailyom.com/journal/ways-to-reparent-your-inner-child-and-heal-from-old-wounds/?aff=910&ad=1&utm_source=google&utm_medium=ppc&utm_campaign=PerformanceMax&acct=9358138875&campaign_id=16896613381&gad_source=1&gclid=CjwKCAiAvoqsBh-B9EiwA9XTWGSZPp3gCBZ_3e5dSH56sjOWmomFaGb-nmIBjms1LE3KaffcTV3UErxhoCdYMQAvD_BwE

What is the subconscious mind? (2020, February 18). Imotions. https://imotions.com/blog/learning/research-fundamentals/what-is-the-subconscious-mind/

Image References

KaylinArt. (2017a). Adult coloring page [Image]. In Pixabay. https://pixabay.com/illustrations/adult-coloring-page-coloring-book-2110236/

KaylinArt. (2017b). Mandala drawing artist pattern [Image]. In Pixabay. https://pixabay.com/illustrations/mandala-drawing-artist-art-pattern-1957618/

Images on the following pages were created with the assistance of DALL-E 2: 76, 112, 120, 131, 132, 138, 165, 176, 184, 208, 220, 233.

Images on the following pages were created with the assistance of Midjourney: 15, 18, 19, 22, 24, 30, 39, 43, 45, 49, 54, 62, 63, 70, 71, 78, 79, 81, 82, 85, 89, 92, 96, 97, 104, 105, 118, 125, 127, 133, 136, 153, 159, 161, 168, 178, 192, 243.

Graphics on the front cover: Designed by Freepik

Made in the USA
Las Vegas, NV
17 February 2025

18256252R00262